I A

Industrial Archaeology

A SERIES EDITED BY
L. T. C. ROLT

3
Roads and Vehicles

Roads and Vehicles

Anthony Bird

Longmans

LONGMANS, GREEN AND CO LTD

London and Harlow
*Associated companies, branches and representatives
throughout the world*

© *Anthony Bird 1969*
First published 1969

SBN: 12614 2

*Printed in Great Britain
by W & J Mackay & Co Ltd, Chatham*

Contents

List of Illustrations

Line Drawings in the Text

Author's Acknowledgements

In addition to those who have helped with the compilation of this book by providing illustrations, and giving permission to reproduce them, my gratitude is also due to Mr Philip Sumner of the Science Museum, South Kensington; to Mr Neil Cossons of the Bristol City Museum; to the Secretary of the Institution of Highway Engineers; to Mr Robin Atthill for permission to reproduce material which had been used to illustrate his book *Old Mendip*; to the Marquess of Anglesey for lending me a copy of the lithograph of his famous ancestor; to Mr L. T. C. Rolt, General Editor of this series, for his help and advice, and to the Librarian at the Fleet Branch of the Hampshire County Libraries who stretched the rules about duration of loans so far on my behalf.

Odiham, 1968   ANTHONY BIRD

Book One

The Roads

CHAPTER ONE

The Background

The admirable precept of the King of Hearts: 'Begin at the beginning', is difficult to follow when dealing with the subject of Industrial Archaeology, or with any aspect of the Industrial Revolution and its many manifestations. Difficult, because no two people agree upon the starting-point. Indeed, it could be argued that there never was any such thing as an Industrial Revolution in the sense of a sudden and dramatic change, a violent break with established methods, but rather a gradual and logical process of evolution which gathered speed as it went, reaching, in our own time, a pace and scale which are truly awful in the original sense of the word. Correct or not, the term 'Industrial Revolution' is now too firmly established to dispute.

There is a school of thought which holds that the starting-point of the great development coincides with the application of steam power to industry. This seems convenient enough, but poses another question. Should one take the date of 1712 when Newcomen erected the first commercially satisfactory steam pumping machine at Dudley, should one settle for 1769 when Watt patented the improvements which more than doubled the efficiency of the atmospheric engine and so made it of practical utility, particularly in remote places where the Newcomen's voracious appetite for fuel put it out of court, or should one fix upon 1783, when the 'rotative' engine at last gave man a more potent source of easily harnessed energy than human, animal or natural forces?

The improvements in communications which gave point and purpose to new inventions and industrial processes did not materialize to any sensible extent until the second half of the eighteenth century; indeed, it was not until the century was nearly spent that real progress began to be made. Therefore the accession of King George III in 1760 may be taken as a convenient, if arbitrary,

3

starting-point for our purpose. There had, of course, been some
improvements to roads and to the vehicles to be found on them
during the previous century, but these were purely local and so
badly co-ordinated that in the seventeenth and early eighteenth
centuries a journey of any length by wheeled carriage was only
slightly less dangerous and fractionally more comfortable than a sea
voyage. In winter the sea traveller might even be better off, because
there was at least a fair chance that his ship would reach its destination eventually, whereas in most parts of the country wheeled traffic
became impossible. As late as 1800 wheeled carts were still virtually
unknown in many of the remoter parts of Scotland, Wales and the
West Country.

The contrast between the civilized, urbane and comfortable way
of life of the eighteenth-century man of reasonable means and his
barbaric and uncertain mode of travelling is startling. Modern man
would find little cause for complaint with the living conditions of his
mid-eighteenth-century ancestor of comparable real income. He
would probably grumble at the inconvenience of reading by candle-
light, and if of egalitarian tendencies he might feel uneasy at the
number of servants to minister to his needs and to keep the domestic machine running. Otherwise he would fit in well enough until
faced with the need to travel in any but perfect summer weather.
Even under ideal conditions he would be appalled by the cost, which
would vary, in present-day terms, from 1s. a mile to as much as £2
a mile, or even more, according to the scale of luxury.

At the upper end of this scale, travelling in some rich nobleman's
private coach escorted by postillions, outriders and footmen, he
might reasonably hope to average four m.p.h. ('if God permit', as
the stage-coach announcements used to say), provided the conveyance
did not break down or overturn in a sea of mud. From such accidents
no amount of wealth could insulate the traveller. When the
Emperor Charles VI visited England in 1703 and essayed to travel
from London to Petworth, not only did the fifty-mile journey take
three days but the imperial coach was overturned a dozen times, and
the journey was only completed by the help of a sufficiency of stout
Sussex labourers who were hired to walk alongside to hold the coach
upright and to put their shoulders to the wheels to force it through
the quagmires.

If the difficulty, danger and expense of personal travelling were formidable, the obstacles hindering goods transport were almost insurmountable. The pack-horse, obviously, could only carry small, light loads, and the movement of heavy or bulky cargoes inland involved great expense, large numbers of draught animals, an inordinate amount of time, and became virtually impossible in wet weather.

As far as possible, therefore, heavy loads went by water, but until the century was nearing its end the canal system, started by Brindley in the 1760s, served only a small part of the country, and many rivers, soon to be made navigable, were still largely un-navigable. Coastwise shipping played a large part and was pressed into service as much as possible, but in many instances it could serve only one leg of a journey and the most straightforward-seeming coastal trip might involve intolerable delays. An example cited by the advocates of the Caledonian Canal was of two ships which left New-castle on the same day, one bound for India by way of the English Channel and the Cape of Good Hope and the other for Liverpool by the Northern route. The Liverpool-bound vessel was so long storm-bound and beset by contrary winds in the Pentland Firth that she took longer to reach her destination than the India-bound ship took to make Bombay.

In view of all the difficulties it is surprising that commerce flourished at all, and amazing not that our ancestors travelled so little but that they travelled so much. The urge to move about was strong in them, though there were, inevitably, those who did not approve. A Mr Cressett, writing in 1662, deplored the increase in the number of stage-coaches which annihilated distance by travelling from Dover to London, a distance of seventy-two miles, in three days: in summer only, of course. Such easy travelling, he said, would encourage country gentlemen to come to London merely to have their hair cut, or for some similarly frivolous purpose. Worse; they would bring their wives, and when man and wife were together in London feminine wiles would urge them to 'get fine clothes, go to plays and treats, and by these means get such a habit of idleness and love of pleasure that they would be uneasy ever after'. Just over a century later the lovable and irascible Matt. Bramble asked: 'Shall I commit myself to the high roads of London or Bristol, to be stifled with dust, or pressed to death in the midst of post-chaises, flying-machines, waggons and coal-horses?' In the eighteenth century anything from a wig-stand to a wheelbarrow could be referred to as a 'machine', and the flying-machines which aroused Mr Bramble's ire were no more than 'fast' coaches, the name having been first applied to steel-sprung vehicles which were advertised to run from London to York and back, in summer, God and weather permitting, at an average speed of 4 m.p.h. This may not seem much like flying by twentieth-century standards, but it was twice as fast as the stage-wagons which carried passengers as well as goods.

A glance at an outline map of Great Britain shows that, unlike most comparable islands, the country is extraordinarily well served with rivers, tributaries and sea inlets of varying degrees of importance. Apart from the main rivers, most of these waterways are small, but most of them are navigable to some extent, and if all the highest points to which loaded boats, even small ones, can be brought were marked on the map it would be seen how small an area of the country is inaccessible by water. With the exceptions of the Pennine Chain, the Lake District and the Border, the whole country is so penetrable that some form of primitive civilization could be carried on by water carriage alone.

As we have seen, the coastal voyaging essential to this water carriage was subject to intolerable delays and inconvenience, but river navigation was also often impossible from natural causes of flood water or low tide, or hindered by man-made obstacles of one sort or another. Those who sought to improve river navigation by embanking, damming, locking or dredging might find themselves in conflict with fishermen and wildfowlers; whilst he who tried to deepen a channel or remove some natural obstacle might find himself brought before the courts by a miller who found his source of power cut off or reduced by the alterations, even though they might be some miles from his mill. Despite all these difficulties, the relative ease of water carriage not only helped establish Great Britain as a sea-trading nation very early but also greatly influenced the development of the road system.

The primary function of the earliest tracks, therefore, was to give access to waterways, but interlinking tracks eventually made it possible to reach all, or nearly all, parts of the country. As far as possible the ancient trackways kept to high ground, and as the only traffic was by foot—human or animal—gradients were of little consequence. Our remote ancestors' need to avoid the valleys as far as possible still influences parts of our road system. The 'modern' road from low-lying Guildford to low-lying Farnham, for example, climbs steeply out of the former town, clings to the ridge of the Hog's Back and then falls less steeply into the latter place, though economy, common sense and Euclid would combine to encourage a twentieth-century road surveyor to plot his course across the valley floor.

Because the dry chalk ridges furnished the easiest going, pre-Roman British civilization was largely based upon a kind of starfish-shaped formation radiating from a central hump on the Salisbury Plain, with its main limbs providing dry going to the Straits of Dover and into Norfolk across the Thames Valley at Streatley, and with lesser limbs penetrating Wiltshire, parts of Somerset, Hampshire and Berkshire. The chalk lands gave our forebears the easiest going, after the waterways, and the clay ridges constituted their most formidable obstacles.

In addition to the engineering difficulty of providing river cross-ings, by ferry, ford or timber bridge, in marshy estuaries the importance of water carriage dictated the placing of the first (often the only) bridge over any navigable stream at the furthest possible point from the sea. This in turn influenced the development of inland towns, such as Oxford, placed at the highest navigable point on a river, and helped to shape the road system.

Under the Romans the extensive network of ancient trackways had a superb system of well-made military roads superimposed upon it. As the function of these roads was primarily to provide the utmost possible mobility for troops in newly conquered territory cost was of secondary importance, and the Roman engineers kept the lines of communication as straight as possible between given points. Curves were avoided and timber cut back to reduce the possibilities of ambush, and on the most important roads only the most formidable obstacles would be avoided by breaks in the direct line. On lesser Roman roads, built later in the occupation, the engineers allowed themselves the luxury of avoiding natural obstacles and therefore these later roads are sometimes almost as tortuous as those which grew up after the Dark Ages.

Military reasons also induced the engineers to raise the roads above the level of the surrounding country where it was possible to do so. Causeways and culverts took care of small streams, but in order not to hinder navigation the Roman engineers did not bridge the lower stretches of navigable rivers, even though, in many instances, their advanced technical resources would have permitted them to do so. Ferries were relied upon in many places, though it is probable that bridges of boats were also used.

Until very recent times the Roman roads were the only real 'trunk routes' this country possessed, and as large sections of them disappeared totally during the Dark Ages (between the fifth and the eleventh centuries) Britain may be said to have been without trunk roads for the best part of a thousand years, and yet became one of the most civilized and prosperous trading nations of western Europe.

As the Roman highways fell into decay traffic reverted to the ancient trackways or made new ones. During the Middle Ages these tracks were, in great degree, widened and improved into roads, and the great increase in wheeled traffic from the end of the sixteenth century onwards provided the impetus for further improvements. These measures, however, stopped short of creating or re-creating trunk roads of uniform gauge and solidity leading as directly as possible from one large centre to the next.

The Civil War, Cromwell's authoritarian government and the struggles to transfer power from the Crown to Parliament (however unrepresentative in present-day terms) sharpened in the British people their marked distaste for any form of interference in local affairs by a central authority: and the provision and maintenance of roads was one of the privileges which local dignitaries, authorities and landowners were particularly reluctant to yield.

A 'main road' journey in Britain therefore consisted of a strange medley of local roads of widely varying standards of construction, repair, width and straightness. There were, indeed, few straight stretches of any distance and these were usually of Roman origin. The 'rolling English road' acquired those continuous, and often apparently inconsequential, changes of direction which are still a feature of many major routes and all our minor roads to this day. They also acquired a wide variety of surfacing materials as soon, that is, as they acquired any at all; for one of the geological peculiarities of Great Britain is the astounding variety of soils and rocks to be found.

It is understandable enough that the Roman roads fell into decay in the absence of any kind of cohesive and regular system of maintaining them, but that large stretches disappeared altogether is less immediately explicable. Until, that is, the rapid spread of marsh and scrub land in a climate such as ours is taken into account. Provided it did not dam the stream the fall of a Roman bridge might still leave the road usable on either side of it and necessitate only the provision of a new path to the nearest fordable place: this was a question more of finding suitable hard banks and approaches rather than a stretch of shallow water. Generally, however, the fall of a bridge presaged the spread of marsh and the damage was worst in places where the road traversed a stream too small to be worthy of a bridge. The crossing of a small stream by embanked viaduct, pierced with culverts, was the breeding-place of many a marsh which altered large areas of country and destroyed many miles of Roman road. It takes very little neglect for a culvert to become choked; the stream then overflows and becomes a pond, the pond water undermines the viaduct, which sinks and becomes a dam and in a very few years the pond becomes a shallow mere surrounded by marsh. Travellers then must make a new pathway by reverting to the ancient method of picking out the driest bits of land no matter how tortuous and haphazard the track from one to another. In the Middle Ages and after, road improvement generally comprised no more than consolidating, widening and, very occasionally, straightening the 'new' routes in such areas, providing new river crossings and leaving the last traces of the old Roman road to sink ever deeper out of sight and mind.

There are many instances of 'artificial' marshes thus formed, even though few traces of them now remain, the boggy land having been drained and reclaimed long since. The area to the south-west of Stamford is one example. Here the Great North Road, the Roman Ermine Street, crossed the Welland about a mile and a half to the west of the present crossing, but the spread of marsh land, following the blocking of the stream, made a wide diversion necessary, and the Great North Road swings away from the original Roman route nearly three miles to the south of the town which grew up around the new crossing-place. Stamford has now been by-passed, after many years of abortive discussion, but it was not possible to follow again the line of the Roman road, as the suburban outskirts of Stamford have completely engulfed its route.

It was not only the 'artificial' marshes which obliterated the road;

similar mishaps occurred in those places where the engineers had had to cross existing marshes on embanked viaducts. A good example may be found in West Sussex where the north-bound Roman road crossed the Arun and its surrounding marshy land at Romans' Wood. This part of the road was raised on a high causeway over heavy clay-bottomed land, and the choking of the culverts led to the collapse of the causeway. The clay lands, thickly covered with thorn scrub, became virtually impassable again. The Roman road from London remained in use as far south as Ockley, but the breakdown of the bridge at Alfoldean produced results similar to those more than twenty miles further south. Except for the most determined travellers, continuity between London and the coast through West Sussex was lost, and for many centuries this large region, though so near the capital, was more isolated than, say, Northumberland. It is significant that West Sussex was one of the last areas of the country to be converted to Christianity and, as the Emperor Charles VI found, it was still a hazardous business to journey from London to Petworth in the early eighteenth century.

Generally speaking, British travellers and their goods went on foot or horseback for the first fifteen hundred years of the Christian era, but wheeled vehicles were not unknown. The Roman conquerors, indeed, had been disconcerted by the British war chariots, but these had no practical use apart from their military function. When faced with the need to shift some burden inland that was too big or heavy to be slung between two pack animals our ancestors had no option but to put it upon a sledge or wheeled cart.

The sledge sufficed for short journeys over really bad terrain and was still in use in remote roadless parts of the British Isles until the nineteenth century; but wheeled carts and wagons were also in use from an early period. They were employed, for instance, in the baggage trains of royalty at the time when the monarch and his court seldom stayed long in one place, but kept constantly on the move throughout the country, supervising administration, collecting taxes and dispensing justice. The royal baggage wagons were moved slowly, with great difficulty and prodigious expenditure of animal power, over rough tracks and through quagmires, frequently breaking down, sticking fast or overturning. Occasionally, as King John found, the utmost exertions of man and beast could not avert total disaster.

Passenger carriages began to be used in the capitals of western Europe in the twelfth century, but they were little used in England until three hundred years later. They were exclusively used by royalty or by ladies of noble birth who were unable to ride, but as they were confined to the few hundred yards of paved streets in important towns their use was strictly limited and, in effect, they were no more than processional carriages—status symbols, in fact. The first passenger coach known to have been built in England was made for the Duke of Rutland in 1555, and Queen Elizabeth commissioned the first State Coach in 1571.

As this was the time of the great expansion of enterprise and inventiveness in Britain, the English, having been slow to start, soon forged ahead. By the end of Queen Elizabeth's reign private carriages were becoming part of every rich man's equipment, and stage-wagons, carrying passengers as well as goods, were plying regularly over certain routes. In summer-time they were able to cover as much as twenty miles a day.

CHAPTER TWO

Highway Administration before **1830**

The administration of the highways in Great Britain has been, until very recently, so chaotic, so inept and so often ludicrous that the pen of a Gibbon wielded with the industry of a Scott could not do justice to it.

Two cardinal points are fundamental and too easily overlooked. Firstly we are easily deceived by the relative scarcity of wheeled vehicles into thinking the traffic in eighteenth-century Britain to have been relatively slight also. The amount of traffic, indeed, was vast, for so small a population, but nearly all of it went on foot; or rather, on hoof, trotter, paw, claw and paddle. In addition to the loads as diverse as fish and flowers, lime and leather, bricks and barometers, cucumbers and coals which were carried by strings of pack animals (and the pack-horse was still the principal vehicle for coal delivery in some districts until the nineteenth century), prodigious herds of cattle, sheep, pigs, geese, turkeys and other livestock were driven along the roads. Towards the end of the eighteenth century as many as 100,000 highland cattle a year were driven south, and between 1776 and 1785 992,040 beef cattle and 6,859,990 sheep were driven to Smithfield Market alone.[1] Anyone who has had half a dozen cows stray across his lawn can visualize the effect of these millions of feet upon soft, unsurfaced roads, but twentieth-century nostrils are mercifully spared the stench which assailed the eighteenth-century nose.

The second point is that originally the 'road' meant a right of passage rather than the track or surface upon which that right could be exercised, and in theory therefore maintenance of the road in the modern sense could not be enforced even had there been any machinery of enforcement. The maintenance of the road in the original sense devolved upon the parishes and, under the remains of the feudal system, upon the individual parishioners. In theory and to some extent in practice this concept of individual responsibility persisted into the nineteenth century and still influenced road legislation into the twentieth.

Under this medieval system it was the duty of each parish to preserve the means of passage for the King, his officers and all his subjects, through the area enclosed by their boundaries, and the gradual process by which the old manorial and feudal rights and duties in this matter had passed to the parish is confused and uncertain. Each parish elected a surveyor of highways to serve for a year without payment, and each surveyor had to extract from each able-bodied man in the parish four days of labour (later raised to six) to keep the ways open. Ultimately he was also able to call upon farmers and some freeholders for horses, carts or materials. It gradually came about that the 'opening of the ways' by cutting undergrowth, lopping or felling trees and clearing culverts in order to relieve floods, came to include rudimentary attention to the surface and structure of the road.

It was generally accepted as inevitable, however, until late in the eighteenth century that many roads would be impassable to wheeled traffic for four or five months in the year at least, and the only remedy the individual traveller, and hence indirectly the central government, had was by 'presentment' or 'indictment' of a parish before the justices in petty session for neglect of a particular stretch of road. The justices might then impose a fine upon the parish to be paid within a given time unless it could be shown that the neglect had been made good. This remedy was difficult to apply and usually ineffective.

In an ideal world unpaid communal labour, using communally provided free materials to provide for the common good would be an ideal system. In the real world it had worked badly even in the heyday of the feudal system when every member of the community had his fixed place in the scheme of things and unalterable rights and duties sanctioned by Church and State under the Common Law; as feudality fell into decay, as the population grew, as society became more fluid, trade more widespread and particularly as wheeled traffic increased it scarcely worked at all.

The first attempt at statutory regulation of these affairs, with the duties of the surveyor of highways defined together with specification of the varying degrees of labour or materials, fines and penalties, to be exacted from differing classes, and the duties of the justices in enforcing, supervising and keeping account was by the Statute of Philip and Mary (2 & 3 Philip and Mary, c. 8), which was passed as a temporary measure in 1555 and permanently re-enacted eight years later by Queen Elizabeth (5 Elizabeth, c. 13). This was not repealed until a codifying Act of George III (7 Geo. III, c. 42, s. 57) re-enacted its principal provisions, and the General Highways Act of 1835 carried on those provisions relating to the surveyor of highways to the end of the nineteenth century.

It was necessary constantly to re-define the annual value of the freeholds and leaseholds which carried the duty of providing teams and carts (Team Duty), and similarly to provide for including or exempting those who were required to furnish the 'Statute Duty', either by personal service or by providing an able-bodied substitute at their own cost. It is scarcely necessary to say that few of those liable for statute duty could afford to pay a deputy. In addition to some hundreds of Turnpike Acts, scores of temporary or amending Acts to the general statutes outlined above were passed to regulate, define, re-define, adjust, complicate (but never to simplify) the details of highway administration without ever altering its essentially medieval basis. Where these Acts attempted also to regulate the traffic, by limiting the number of horses which should draw a given weight, for example, or by attempting to regulate the design and construction of vehicles, the emphasis was always upon adjusting the vehicle to suit the road and the notion that it might be proper to make roads to suit the traffic was firmly resisted by legislators, national and local, until the nineteenth century was well advanced. Except for the Post Office no government department lent more than token support to road improvement in England, though in the Scottish Highlands and in Ireland road construction was embarked upon as a government measure to relieve distress and prevent depopulation.

The statute of Philip and Mary particularly defined the duties of the surveyor of highways and made it obligatory (instead of merely customary) for each parish to appoint some luckless person to this office annually. The duties of the local justices and of certain of the owners of lands adjacent to the roads, and of the constable and other parish officers were also defined, together with the scale upon which these individuals could be fined for neglect of their duties. Above these individual obligations, the obligation of the parish as a whole to maintain its roads was codified; unless it could be shown that some person or corporate body was legally liable for a particular stretch of road it was the statutory duty of every able-bodied person to play some part. Women were not specifically excluded at first, but later modifying Acts made it clear that in those rare cases where women were house- or freeholders certain exemptions would apply. In addition to the legal liability of the parish officers, the parish as a whole could be presented before the justices and fined for neglect.

All the labour, tools and materials had to be provided gratuitously by the parishioners at the demand of the surveyor, who was thus bound to fall foul of his neighbours: also, 'every person for every plough land in tillage or pasture' (later defined as any holding of £50 or more annual value) and 'every person keeping a draught of horses or plough in the Parish' had to provide and send 'one wain or cart furnished after the custom of the country, with oxen, horses or other cattle, and all other necessaries meet to carry things convenient for that purpose, and also two able men with the same'. Those of a lower rank who had to furnish only their labour were described in this Act as: 'Every other householder, cottager or labourer able to labour and being no hired servant by the year.' Those unable to attend on the days appointed by the surveyor had to send 'one sufficient labourer' in their stead. Not less than eight hours were to be worked on four (later six) consecutive days.

In addition to being exceedingly inefficient, this system was particularly unpopular. The days of labour, necessarily summer days, inevitably interrupted work which was considered of greater importance; labourers had either to forgo six days' earnings or hire substitutes which they could not afford; richer men, farmers and landowners, had to spare horses and carts from their own concerns and each felt he was being unfairly treated by comparison with his neighbour. It says much for the English hatred of interference with individual liberty by a central authority that this parochial system lasted so long, but every attempt to place highway administration under some larger and more efficient unit of control was fiercely resisted. Even Cromwell did not succeed in altering the system, though among the business being discussed just before his peremptory dismissal of Parliament in 1657 was a Bill for Repairing of the Highways and Improving the Public Roads; in anticipation of which

the Lord Protector had already appointed, by patent, a Surveyor-
General of Highways, who was to have large funds at his disposal
(and, said the Bill's opponents, opportunity to pocket £10,000 a year
himself) and authority throughout the kingdom. The Bill was
vociferously opposed.[2]

The obligations to furnish team duty and statute duty were
naturally evaded as much as possible. Naturally, also, those least able
to bear the brunt were least successful in escaping it. In typically
English fashion when a team was assembled for enforced labour on
the roads the individual grumbles tended to coalesce into a collective
mood of jollification; instead of a body of malcontents shirking
their work from a sense of grievance, the harassed surveyor would
find himself trying to organize a pack of skylarking neighbours who
shirked their work because of a sudden onrush of holiday spirits.

From an early period the statute labour could be supplemented by,
and eventually commuted for, money payments raised by a parish
rate, authorized by the justices, for which the surveyor was account-
able. By the middle of the eighteenth century money had been
substituted for direct labour in many parishes, but as the highway
rate was limited to 6d. or 1s. in the pound the funds were always
insufficient, and the other shortcomings of total want of co-ordination
between one parish and the next and the inefficiency of the surveyors
remained unaltered. Towards the end of the eighteenth century, and
during the first quarter of the nineteenth, many parishes tried the
expedient of using the highway rate to relieve the demands on
the poor rate; but this did not make for efficiency, as all too often the
paupers put to mend the roads were paupers because they could not
or would not work.

The principle of levying a county rate for road work was very
occasionally adopted, though there seems to have been no sanction
for it. In a rare pamphlet in the British Museum[3] the author cites:
'what hath lately been done in Kent, upon Canterbury road, which
they have made very substantially good where it was extremely bad
before, by a small tax of about a halfpenny in the pound laid upon
the County'.

It was upon the surveyor of highways that the chief burden fell
and he was at the root of all maladministration; his was indeed an
unenviable task. By the original Statute and subsequent amendments
various classes such as the clergy, landed proprietors above a certain

small value, lawyers, militiamen and the holders of 'Tyburn Tickets' (i.e. those granted exemption from certain obligations for a term of years in consideration of having helped bring a felon to justice) were all at various times exempt. In other words, the men most likely to have leisure and education enough for the efficient discharge of the office were never called upon to execute it, and in practice the surveyor was usually a small farmer, tradesman or possibly an innkeeper and was not, consequently, of sufficient stature to withstand coercion or to call an influential backsliding neighbour to account.

As a money system gradually displaced the communal and gratuitous basis of providing men and materials, it increasingly fell to the surveyor's lot to be a buying and accountancy expert, in which fields his lack of knowledge equalled his ignorance of road engineering, but which opened to him an avenue for peculation. By the end of the eighteenth century it became customary for many parishes to pay their surveyor a small honorarium, and it was often found that the surveyorship had been conferred as a means of paying a pension to some incapacitated (or even bedridden) local worthy. On the whole, however, as the evidence before innumerable Parliamentary Committees makes clear, there was surprisingly little dishonesty but a vast deal of incompetence in the financial administration by the surveyors, coupled, generally, with their total incompetence in practical administration.

This incompetence is understandable: with a few honourable exceptions (of which John Loudon McAdam is the most notable) none of these surveyors was in a position to know anything of road-making or surveying despite their somewhat misleading title. In many parishes, indeed, the statutory designation was ignored and the surveyor was known more aptly as the overseer, waywarden or boonmaster: boon in this context being 'work given gratuitously'. It was repeatedly urged in Parliament that no improvement would be made to the roads whilst unpaid, amateur and often illiterate surveyors were responsible for them. An Act of 1766 (7 Geo. III, c. 42, s. 2), re-enacted in 1773 (13 Geo. III, c. 78, s. 5) provided that if two-thirds of the ratepayers agreed they might nominate a paid surveyor and provide his wages from the 'composition' moneys arising from the commutation of statute labour and fines or penalties in connection therewith.

It was also provided that if a parish failed to appoint an unpaid surveyor (and many did), or if the chosen man refused to serve and no alternative could be found (another common happening) the justices could appoint a surveyor of their choice and order the parish to pay him one-eighth of the sixpenny rate. At the same time they were empowered to appoint an assistant from the parishioners, who was to be compelled to serve gratuitously under the paid official. This provision was stigmatized by one of the leading authorities of the day[4] as: '. . . likely to produce private animosity instead of public benefit'. As far as can be discovered, however, no animosity was generated, as this part of the law was never implemented. During the last years of the eighteenth century, though, it became not uncommon for the larger parishes to pay their surveyors, which effected some trifling improvements; though the smallness of the salaries and the lack of co-ordination between parishes prevented real progress.

All other considerations apart, the annual change of surveyor (and whilst the job was unpaid few would undertake a second term of office) was an almost total bar to improvement. As John Scott[5] wrote:

The annual choice of Surveyors is in itself an impropriety. There are perhaps few offices wherein more skill and attention are required . . . yet before this officer is half master of his business, he is discharged and a fresh ignoramus chosen; consequently the work is never done as it ought to be.

Subsequent observers, writers, pamphleteers and witnesses before Parliamentary Committees reiterated the burden of Scott's appraisal to an almost wearisome extent. In addition to the cumbersome remedy of indictment or presentment, other remedies had been put in the hands of the justices by Parliament, and the extreme rarity with which the law was set in motion suggests that the lay magistracy was as ignorant and neglectful as the parish officers. This is not quite just, and those masterly chroniclers of the history of local government, Sidney and Beatrice Webb[6] have summed it up:

. . . all the indirect evidence indicates that, as in the case of the prisons and the Poor Law, the vast majority of the eighteenth century magistrates never realised that they had any administrative responsibility at all for the management of the roads.

They persisted in regarding themselves as a judicial tribunal, called upon only to listen to such complaints as might be brought before them of any positive breach of the law, and then impartially to adjudicate. So little did the Justices exercise their power of appointing surveyors that it came habitually to be supposed that their duty was limited to the formal ratification of the choice [of the] vestries . . . in the consolidating Highway Acts of 1766–73 the useful power to insist on written reports being handed in by every surveyor at every meeting was omitted—apparently by mere inadvertence—and this goes a long way to prove that listening to and criticising . . . these forms had not actually formed part of the business of the typical bench of magistrates.

The magistrates were also reluctant to enforce the statute duty or payment of composition money upon ordinary citizens; this underlines a fact too often forgotten, which is that the severity of the penal code in the eighteenth century, and the oppression the poor suffered by the operation of harsh laws, were mitigated by the natural humanity of those who administered the law. Sir John Hawkins,[7] himself a magistrate, wrote of the notorious reluctance to enforce the statute duty:

Consider the excuses of the poor man—poverty, a numerous family . . . sickness, lameness and an income of nine shillings a week . . . and think whether that authority is to be envied which the magistrates are sworn to exert in enforcing obedience to perhaps one of the most oppressive statutes that ever yet received the sanction of public assent.

Similar tenderness was often extended towards the negligent surveyor, who was so often a neighbour and probably a tenant of the presiding justice, and only when some busybody from outside 'presented' a parish for default was the full machinery put into action. Here again, though the offending parish might be repeatedly fined, the fines were almost always a form of 'suspended sentence' to be remitted if it were shown that the default had been made good: and most benches would, it seems, accept a mere token improvement.

It is now fashionable to look upon the turnpike trusts and their

influence on highway development as embodiments of all the most
pernicious features of a profit-seeking capitalist society. To progressive social historians it is anathema that stretches of public road
could be leased to private speculators who were empowered to mulct
travellers of relatively large fees in return for which they offered
rather nebulous improvements whilst remaining virtually exempt
from legal sanction if they defaulted on their bargain. A dismal picture may be drawn of trade throttled; of by-ways being closed so that
local traffic was forced to take the expensive and probably circuitous
turnpike road; of greedy landowners dominating the trusts, growing rich out of illicit pickings and misusing their powers to divert
roads in order to preserve their own demesnes or sporting interests.

The turnpike system had many shortcomings, but most of its
failings, like those of the parish system, were occasioned by incompetence rather than dishonesty on the part of the trustees. To
deal first with the 'profit motive', it is enough to say that few trusts
accumulated profits; most were heavily in debt and many were
bankrupt. In those places where reasonable administration and brisk
traffic did yield a profit the statutory limitations were sufficient (and
sufficiently enforced) to keep the hands of individual trustees out
of the till. No doubt there were some instances where a particular
piece of road was improved or even diverted to the particular benefit
of an individual trustee (or perhaps to thwart some other), but very
little evidence of this sort of malpractice can be found.

Dishonesty in turnpike administration was at a level below that
of the trustees. Although the 'pike keepers' were reasonably paid by
the standards of the time they exercised the inalienable right of the
working man to swindle their employers. The trusts had practically
no way of assessing what was properly due to them except by sending
trustees, or chosen representatives, to take a day's duty at one of the
toll houses so that they could gauge an average day's takings. This,
obviously, was tantamount to setting the regular toll collectors a
maximum which they never thereafter exceeded no matter how
much the traffic on that route might grow. Despairing of finding
honest toll-takers most trusts adopted the trouble-saving but money-
wasting expedient of farming the tolls; that is, the rights would be
leased, generally by the year, to the toll-farmer who naturally
secured his profit by paying a rent or fee considerably below the
lowest estimated value of the toll receipts.

The principle of adapting the traffic to suit the roads was favoured by turnpike trustees, who were empowered by their Acts of Parliament to adjust the tolls on complex sliding scales which took account of weight in relation to the number of horses and the width of the wheels (see Chapter 5). The 'overcharges' were very severe; an additional hundredweight over a set limit, or tyres an inch narrower than was suitable for a given load might increase the toll twentyfold. To calculate these charges the principal turnpike routes were furnished with cumbersome weighing 'engines' which gave rise to further peculation. The 'engine keepers' would compound with wagoners for the overcharge money and the trusts were defrauded of vast sums on this account. Just as the tolls were farmed, the rights in the weighing engines were also let annually, usually by public auction, and as the rents paid were often two or three times the theoretical maximum annual value of the weighing fees it is clear that this form of robbery was practised on a large scale. The 'engines', incidentally, were not like modern weighbridges, but were large timber structures, always getting out of order, which combined the functions of crane and steelyard, and the vehicles were actually winched off the ground for weighing.

If it be accepted that it was the English love of individual liberty and hatred of interference by central authority in local affairs which perpetuated the parochial system, it might seem odd that the turnpike trusts, established by Act of Parliament, were accepted initially with little opposition. Here were bodies outside local control authorized to divert and alter local roads, to stop up by-ways, to erect barriers and toll-houses and to levy a tax upon travellers. In the seventeenth century certain parishes bordering the ancient highway from London to York had found the maintenance of the road, with its steadily increasing traffic, altogether beyond their resources. The Vestry of Radwell in Hertfordshire petitioned the Quarter Sessions for relief and in due time the County Justices of Hertford, Cambridge and Huntingdon represented to Parliament that the road, despite the best effort of the parishes, had become 'ruinous and almost impassable' because of 'the great and many loads which are weekly drawn in waggons'. Each of the three Quarter Sessions for the counties concerned were empowered by statute (15 Car. II, c. 1) of 1663 to put up gates at Wadesmill, Caxton and Stilton and to exact tolls to provide funds for the upkeep of those parts of the trunk road that ran through the three counties. These provisions aroused furious opposition; the gate at Stilton, in consequence, was never put to use, that at Caxton was easily evaded and Wadesmill represented the first effective toll-gate in Britain.

Despite the opposition, and the relative ineffectiveness of the scheme, similar powers were granted to the Justices of Essex, Norfolk, Surrey, Gloucestershire, Somerset, Cheshire, Bedfordshire, Wiltshire, Hampshire and Kent. Towards the end of the seventeenth century therefore it appeared that the county justices would become the country's highway authorities acting either in Quarter Sessions or in special Highway Sessions; but this logical trend was suspect and was diverted in 1706 when the first turnpike trust was set up to keep and mend the road between Fornhill in Bedfordshire and Stony Stratford in Buckinghamshire.

To the mind of the eighteenth-century Member of Parliament, so nervous of the executive, the notion of making the local landed proprietors responsible for the roads by the creation of trusts seemed infinitely preferable to any centralized system, whether controlled by the counties or otherwise. From this small beginning in 1706 the turnpike system grew quickly, and a century later more than 1,100 trusts were responsible for 23,000 miles of road put in order or newly made at the cost of an accumulated debt of £7,000,000 and calling for the annual expenditure of £1,500,000.[8] One of the major weaknesses of the system was that the trusts invariably had to borrow money for their initial operations, partly by issuing bonds and largely by pledging their revenues, and much of the money which should have been spent on the roads went in servicing their debts; for Parliament set no limit on the amounts they might borrow.

That the turnpike trusts at first aroused less hostility than the earlier county toll system is easily understood. The formation of a trust was usually instigated by some local landowner or nobleman acting, as so many did, largely in the public interest in default of any other way of getting things done: the trustees were drawn from others of his kind with an admixture of the smaller squires, large farmers, retired service officers and the like, with, probably, the local attorney to act as secretary and treasurer. The trusts were invariably given power to co-opt extra members almost *ad lib.* and thus all the local worthies could be given opportunities for self-aggrandisement. In this way the trust could be sure of support from

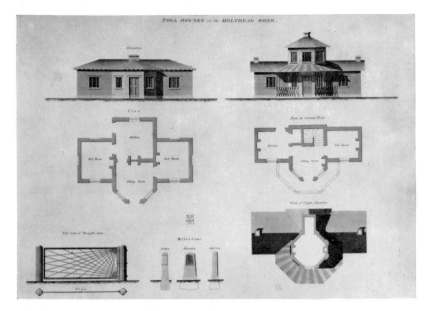

1 Telford's designs for toll-houses, milestones and iron turnpike gates for the Holyhead Road

2 One of the surviving toll-houses, Holyhead Road

3 A Telford gate now guards the entrance to the lane to
Glan 'r Afon near Llangernyw

4 One of Telford's mile-stones   5 Weigh house and toll-board
                                          near Llangollen

the most vocal part of the community; no tolls were allowed to be charged on foot passengers and so the poorest travellers had no grievance, and the inhabitants of parishes through which the turnpike road passed had reason to suppose that they would be relieved of their statute labour and team duties (or the composition money) in respect of that road. Consequently they, too, saw no need to oppose the innovation, particularly as arrangements were always made to free essential agricultural traffic from tolls.

The parishioners' hopes that their burdens might be lifted were soon dashed, as it became clear that Parliament had no intention of abolishing statute labour and team duty in relation to the turnpikes. The new turnpike surveyors were required to pay for labour and materials at the prevailing rates for the initial repair or construction of a road, but in matters of upkeep they were soon given almost as many powers as the parish surveyors, with the addition of the backing of the powerful body of trustees. From 1714 onwards the turnpike surveyor was given express power to exact the performance, under his own direction, of a proportion (usually one-third) of the statute labour and team duty of the parishioners. He was also authorized to take gravel, stone, chalk and other materials from the common lands, without payment, or from private ground merely on payment for incidental damage. Though never empowered to raise a money rate, as other local authorities were, the trusts were authorized to demand a lump sum from the parishes in lieu of statute labour; thus they received money from the parishes as well as from the tolls.

The greatest injustice was that the old system of financing repair of a neglected stretch of road, by indictment of the parish, was retained, and the unhappy parishioners might find themselves before the court for the neglect of a body in whose affairs they had no say. It is true that under the General Highways Act of 1773 the court could apportion the fine and costs between the parish and the trust, but there was an escape clause for the trust in that it was enacted that the parish should pay the full charge and recover the portion due from the trust only if it could be done 'without endangering the security of the creditors who have advanced money upon the credit of the Tolls'. As practically every trust had mortgaged its tolls to the full, the parishes could not be reimbursed.

The injustice was so flagrant that the magistrates were extremely reluctant to proceed, and the device of indictment as a means of making good a neglected road became less effective than ever. Nevertheless, indictments were frequent and the turnpike trusts became so unpopular that sporadic rioting broke out in different parts of the country, becoming eventually so serious that destruction of a toll-gate was made a capital offence.

The local justices and gentry who sat on the trusts and formed so large a body in Parliament were, indeed, fully conscious of the many injustices suffered by the parishioners; but this consciousness never manifested itself in an attempt to change the fundamental basis of the law, but was seen in a long string of Highway Acts, and in minor alterations to each Turnpike Act as it fell due for renewal (most turnpikes were restricted to a life of twenty-one years and had then to apply to Parliament for a new Act), which tinkered with the law as it stood, generally by the favourite expedient of regulating the traffic to fit the roads. The legislation became so confused that the best legal authorities of the eighteenth century confessed themselves unable to make sense of the mass of definitions, re-definitions, regulations, exemptions and contradictions which made up the corpus of highway law. Writing on one aspect alone, the number of beasts permitted to a given load and the manner of their harnessing, Dr Burn[9] wrote in 1755:

> If a person would know what number of horses or beasts in a cart or waggon are allowed by the statutes for the preservation of the roads, let him take what treatise at present he pleases concerning the highways, he must read over the whole, before he shall be sure he hath found all which the law hath enacted concerning the same; and such is often the inaccuracy and confusion, that when he hath perused the whole, . . . he may be still to seek, for, as to this instance before us, there have been regulations made . . . by ten different Acts of Parliament . . . Before he can have any competent knowledge thereof he must lay all these ten Acts together, and when he shall have done this, he will find amongst them so many repeals and revivals and explanations that even then it will be no easy matter to conclude with certainty how the law doth stand as to that article.

In general, therefore, the attitude of Parliament to the highways may be summed up as one which clung to the once-admirable notion of individual responsibility long after it had become untenable, and which regarded traffic in general and wheeled traffic in particular as an 'active nuisance . . . to be suppressed in its most noxious forms and, where inevitable, to be regulated and restricted as much as possible', as Sidney and Beatrice Webb express it. The same writers go on to say:

> Instead of the modern purpose of providing such roads as secure the maximum mobility of men and commodities, our great-grandfathers aimed at preserving their highways from anything beyond the minimum wear and tear. Indeed, from the middle of the eighteenth century onwards they thought they could make the traffic positively subservient to the maintenance of the road by converting every wheeled vehicle into an involuntary roller . . . It is only by realising the implicit assumption, that the existing soft highways were to be protected against the intrusion of wheeled traffic, that the complicated and long continued legislation as to wheels . . . can be seen to lack neither ingenuity nor a certain equitable justification.

Justification, that is, in theory, for in practice the legislation governing wheel-widths never served its intended purpose.

In the framing of the original Turnpike Acts it was assumed that the term of (usually) twenty-one years would suffice to put the road in order and so organize its maintenance that the ordinary parish rates or statute labour would be enough for its subsequent well-being, so that the tolls could be discontinued and the bars and toll-houses dismantled. In effect this did not happen; because of the incompetence of most turnpike surveyors; because of the wasteful farming of tolls necessitated by the dishonesty of the toll-takers; because of the interest on the mortgaged incomes and because of the instincts of self-aggrandisement among the trustees, the trusts became self-perpetuating and almost invariably applied for renewal of their Acts. This involved a further wastage of money, as very large fees and other expenses were incurred (such as the need to keep lawyers and treasurers in London throughout parliamentary sessions) and Parliament would not yield to the repeated pleas that it was unjust to charge as large fees for the renewal of an Act as for the initial drafting and enactment. A not inconsiderable proportion of every trust's income lined the pockets of attorneys, parliamentary agents, clerks and other officials who were all entitled to fees of one sort or another.

Despite their many shortcomings, the turnpike trusts did useful work which, given the eighteenth-century attitude to administration, probably could not have been done by other means. They made possible the remarkable speeds and regularity of road travel at the heyday of the coaching era, and from innumerable references in books, journals and letters it is clear that the traveller on wheels welcomed each stretch of turnpike road with the same warmth his motoring descendant accords to each stretch of dual carriage way.

This melioration of passenger traffic was important enough, but by no means so vital as the part the turnpike system played in the Industrial Revolution by making it possible for wheeled goods vehicles to move in many places where they had formerly been unable to struggle through the quagmires of the parish roads. When it is remembered that the most a pack-horse could carry was about two hundredweight, and that the same horse could draw ten or twelve hundredweight on wheels, given a reasonable surface, there is no need to say more.

The turnpikes not only affected every aspect of national life, but left their visible signs on the countryside, some of which remain. As the traffic increased the constant checks for toll-taking became less and less tolerable, but it seemed as though 'pike' and toll-house were permanent fixtures on the scene. The first turnpike gates had been in the form of tapered, lance-like, counterbalanced bars, pivoted at the point of balance so as to swing horizontally across the roadway on a suitable upright post. Hence the name 'Turn Pike', but although minor roads debouching on a main thoroughfare were still closed by similar 'side bars' in the nineteenth century, normal gates soon replaced the original swinging 'pikes'.

Near each gate stood the toll-house or 'pike-keeper's' cottage. At first, no doubt, a mere wooden hut sufficed, but as it became clear that the trusts would be more than merely temporary expedients neat little houses of brick or local stone were built. As the average eighteenth-century builder, no matter how humble, seems to have been incapable of producing an ill-proportioned structure, most toll-houses were attractive as well as functional. The interior fitments usually included a built-in till for the toll money and in at least one instance this was ingeniously made part of the kitchen dresser.

Toll-house architecture naturally varied according to locality and period, but most trusts adopted a uniform style not only for their toll-houses but for their gates, milestones, lanterns and other 'furniture'. The houses were often so designed and angled as to give the widest possible view of the approaches, and were usually given wide projecting eaves, at least on the gateward side, so that the pike-keeper could have some shelter as he took the tolls in wet weather. Charming hexagonal buildings were not uncommon, and the mock-Gothic touches, so surprisingly well suited to cottage architecture, often adorned and emphasized casements and door-cases.

Where a toll-house stood on or near some grand estate a more imposing structure than the usual cottage was often built—sometimes, apparently, at the landowner's expense. A splendid example was the battlemented 'folly' on the Newbury-Hungerford road just west of Speen. This has recently been demolished, though it was in good repair and stood in nobody's way. It is somehow typical of our national architectural blindness that this delightful building has gone whilst the ugly, crumbling, brick bug-hutch which served as a toll-house opposite the Spaniards Inn on Hampstead Heath has been lovingly preserved, though it is admittedly devoid of aesthetic merit and has been notorious for the traffic jams it creates (as it juts far out into a narrow road) for more than a century. The task of tracing the old turnpike and parish roads, of recording the sites of vanished toll-houses, or of preserving the few good ones which remain, is at last receiving attention from archaeological societies and individual enthusiasts for industrial archaeology.

The turnpike trusts and their methods of working grew up in a haphazard way. It is now fashionable to deride the English talent for improvisation, and to regard the ability to make the best of a bad job as a negative virtue; but these qualities were brought to bear on our highways, and our forebears who found themselves encumbered with an incredibly bad system contrived to make it work much better than it had any business to do.

The stimulus was provided by the mail-coach, ably seconded by the stage-coaches which emulated it, and in the thirty years following that fateful Monday, 2 August 1784, when the first mail-coach left Bristol, more was done to improve the roads than in the previous three hundred years.

Nevertheless the lack of any effective means of dealing with neglected highways was still a serious drawback, and in places where the physical difficulties were greatest, as in Wales and Scotland, the resources were least. As late as 1808 the Postmaster-General's attempt to extend the mail-coach service from Shrewsbury to Holyhead was frustrated by the badness of the Welsh roads: so bad were they that even the riding-post had difficulty in getting through, and three post-horses fell and broke their legs in one winter week.[10] Indicting the responsible parishes and trusts was tried but was of little avail, for the Welsh turnpike trusts were heavily in debt and the maximum penalties, unjust though they would have been, could not have produced the money needed for the task.

Because of the urgent need to improve communication with Ireland, and particularly because of the energy of Sir Henry Parnell, M.P. for Queen's County, a Holyhead Road Commission was set up, and Telford's great trunk road, the first to deserve the name, was financed and constructed on a national scale.

The physical construction or reconstruction of this vital highway is dealt with in Chapter 4: administratively, the pattern set in Scotland and Ireland (where urgent social problems and the need to prevent depopulation had spurred Government to play a direct part in road-making) was repeated. With Telford as their surveyor and engineer, the Highland Road Commission had successfully opened hitherto inaccessible regions, and in 1810 a Special Committee of the House of Commons recommended similar measures to improve communication with Ireland by way of the London-Holyhead road: this meant almost total replanning and rerouting of the Shrewsbury to Holyhead portion. The Act of Union had sharpened the need to improve Irish communications, and public and commercial discontent with the existing state of the road reinforced the Postmaster-General's insistence that the whole of this route must be made fit for coaches.

The success Telford had had in overcoming gradients and bridging streams in the Highlands made his appointment to the Holyhead Commission almost automatic. He surveyed the route in minute detail on behalf of the body of ten Commissioners which Parliament had incorporated by a special Act; three Ministers of the Crown sat on this Commission, but Sir Henry Parnell, M.P. (later Lord Congleton), was its head and front. He it was who drafted and piloted the innumerable local Bills through Parliament which were needed to deal with the different local authorities, and he it was who persuaded Parliament to vote £20,000 to supplement the inadequate resources of the parishes and turnpike trusts involved.

There were twenty-three different turnpike trusts concerned, each of which had to be persuaded, argued with and cajoled into allowing the Government's Surveyor to organize the reconstruction of their stretch of road. The seventeen English trusts were left nominally in control, although those of Whetstone and St Albans (whose portions of the road were notoriously bad) only came to heel under threat of a special Act of Parliament to empower the Commissioners to take their affairs in hand for a term of years; but Telford had the real authority to lower an ascent, embank a slough, cut through a hill or build a bridge as circumstances dictated. The Local Acts gave power to the individual trusts to raise their tolls by 50 per cent, once the work was done, and from the increased revenue they were obliged to reimburse the Commission.

Stronger measures had to be taken in Wales, where six trusts administered the worst eighty-five miles of the route and had neither the will nor the means to do what was necessary. By patient and tactful negotiation, spread over many months, Sir Henry Parnell persuaded these six trusts to surrender their powers and revenues, under a special Act of Parliament, to one body of fifteen trustees. By the same Act the new consolidated trust was obliged to appoint a professional civil engineer to plan and execute the work needed.

With all these negotiations in and out of Parliament, together with the physical difficulty of the work in the remote and mountainous regions, it is scarcely surprising that the Holyhead road project took twenty years to complete and that it cost the then staggering sum of £750,000; though this total did include rebuilding Holyhead harbour and the unprecedented engineering feat of bridging the Menai Strait.

Inspired, perhaps, by Sir Henry Parnell's success, Viscount Lowther, M.P., moved for a Committee of Inquiry in the House of Commons to investigate the turnpikes in and near the capital. He alleged that since the beginning of the century traffic had increased to such an extent that £200,000 a year was being paid in tolls within a ten-mile radius of St Paul's, but that mismanagement and servicing the funded debts absorbed seven-tenths of this sum. As a result of this inquiry an Act was passed in 1826 to consolidate fourteen of the Middlesex Trusts into one body which became responsible for 172 miles of London streets and approach roads with an average annual toll income of £65,000.

This modest measure of consolidation yielded good results, and the device of a parliamentary grant had shown what could be done on the Holyhead road. The time seemed ripe for similar action elsewhere, and the municipalities of Newcastle, York and Hull, together with the principal Yorkshire landowners, induced the Government to allow the Postmaster-General to appoint Telford to survey the whole line of the Great North Road from London to Edinburgh with a view to reconstruction on the Holyhead model. His survey started in 1827 and his plan included proposals to shorten the distance between the two capitals by more than twenty miles. Gradients were to be eased, corners cut, the road made of uniform width and the worst stretch of tortuous, narrow lane (for it was no more) over the hundred miles from Peterborough to York was to become as straight as a Roman road. The House of Commons' Special Committee accepted the plan, and proposed to follow the Holyhead precedent in order to give it effect. To the inevitable howls of protest from the turnpike trusts were added petitions from towns and villages, whose inhabitants feared either that they would be left high and dry by the alterations or that their peaceful seclusion would be ruined by through traffic. Parliament was necessarily influenced by these objections and was alarmed at the cost of the project, but might nevertheless have passed the Northern Road Bill if the scale had not been tipped by an apparently insignificant incident. This was the trial of locomotives at Rainhill in 1829, the resounding success of Stephenson's *Rocket* and the consequent decision to use steam power for all traffic on the Liverpool to Manchester Railway.

The railway age was about to begin in earnest, the short heyday of the road coach was nearly over, Telford's grand north road was never built and direct intervention by Government in highway planning and construction was abandoned again for eighty years.

CHAPTER THREE

Highway Administration after 1830

Many scores of Bills touching on highway matters were presented to Parliament during the second quarter of the nineteenth century, but we need concern ourselves only with the few which attempted fundamental changes in the system. It is important to remember that even during the heyday of the turnpike trusts many thousands of miles of road, including several important through-routes, remained in the sole jurisdiction of each 'parish, township, tithing, rape, vill, wapentake, division, city, borough, liberty, market-town, franchise, hamlet or chapelry', as the General Highways Act of 1835 put it.

This Act (5 & 6 William IV, c. 50) marked a great step forward. The ancient obligation to give service in kind, by statute labour and team duty, was at last abolished and all the restrictive and contradictory regulations about wheel widths in relation to weight, numbers of horses and lines of draught were repealed.

The modern system of using salaried officials and labour hired at the market rate (for the use of pauper labour which many parishes had enthusiastically adopted had proved a failure) was established, but the other vital improvement, enlarging the administrative area, urged by every Parliamentary Committee, pamphleteer and interested observer, was not embarked upon. The advantages of larger units were obvious; chief among them were the possibility of apportioning costs according to the importance of the roads, a more equitable way of spreading the burden, and the possibility of providing tasks and salaries of sufficient scope to attract experienced surveyors and engineers. It would have been logical if the 1835 Act had harked back to the notion tentatively (and successfully) tried in the seventeenth century of making each county into an administrative highway area with the Quarter Sessions as the governing authority.

There were three reasons why this was not done. Firstly the Government of 1835 was Whig and therefore unwilling to increase the powers of the county justices, who were predominantly Tory. Secondly it was contrary to Whig principles to give new powers of raising rates to non-elective bodies, particularly since the relatively great sums the counties had had to raise for modernization of jails and lunatic asylums had made them very unpopular. The third reason was rather less tainted by party expediency; this was the hostility some county justices had incurred by exercising powers given under an Act of 1815 whereby any two of them could close any footpath they deemed unnecessary. The growth of towns and manufacturing districts had led to abuse of rights of way over private lands by the working people, but in closing paths some magistrates had inexcusably abused their powers from selfish motives. The enmity this had aroused influenced Parliament against giving the counties jurisdiction over highways.

The 1835 Act, therefore, left some 15,000 'highway parishes' (half of them containing fewer than fifty families within their boundaries) responsible for spending more than £1,000,000 a year (subject only to the amateurish audit of the local bench) in the maintenance of more than 100,000 miles of road. The parishes were empowered to combine, in the interests of economy, into larger 'highway districts', sharing a common surveyor; but few of them would surrender their autonomy, though a handful of them, mostly in municipalities, did take advantage of a clause in the Act which permitted them to elect 'highway boards'. These were, in effect, executive subcommittees of the vestries to supervise road construction and repair.

In addition to the 15,000 parishes there were, in 1838, 1,116 turnpike trusts, maintaining 22,000 miles of highway, employing 3,555 treasurers, clerks and surveyors, in addition to 20,000 toll-collectors. Their toll receipts, from 7,796 gates and side-bars, amounted to £1,458,000 of which approximately £51 was spent on each mile of road, the remainder being used partly to pay interest on some £7,000,000 of funded debt and the rest lost through peculation and inefficiency. By contrast the 104,700 miles of parochial roads administered by the parishes had only £11 spent on each mile.[1]

It was by a combination of flukes and accidents that the next developments came. The first of these arose from a wave of public resentment against inefficient administration and dishonest toll-farming on behalf of some of the turnpike trusts in South Wales. So acutely were local passions aroused by these 'farmers', who had multiplied their gates and erected side-bars so that local agricultural traffic, supposedly exempt from toll, was improperly taxed, that a series of riots broke out in the winter of 1842–43 which led to extensive demolition of toll-houses and gates throughout South Wales. Inspired by Genesis 24:60, in which it is promised to the wife of Isaac that her descendants shall hold the gate of her enemies, the rioters arrayed themselves in women's clothes and called themselves 'Rebecca and her Children'.[2] A great deal of damage was done and many of the gate-keepers lost all their belongings when the toll-houses were pulled down and fired, but although such crimes were nominally capital ones the authorities quite rightly saw where the blame really rested. The rioters were leniently treated (most were merely bound over to keep the peace) and the Home Secretary, Sir James Graham, that most enlightened of Tory reformers, drafted and carried an Act through Parliament which summarily dismissed the responsible trustees and merged the offending South Wales trusts into county road boards, appointed by Quarter Sessions.

These boards took over the roads, the tolls and the debts; many of the gates and side-bars were abolished and the most significant aspect of the organization was that the boards were guided in technical matters by a 'General Superintendent of County Roads in South Wales', who was appointed by the Home Secretary. The roads were greatly improved, nearly £250,000 was advanced by the Treasury, the debts were consolidated into terminable annuities bearing $3\frac{1}{4}$ per cent interest and by a combination of honest management (the toll-farmers having gone) and the 'economies of scale' the boards not only paid their way but discharged their bond debts in thirty years.

During this thirty years it was proposed many times that this pattern, so fortuitously but so successfully drawn as a result of the 'Rebecca Riots', should be generally followed, but the timidity of successive Home Office officials combined with the indifference of successive Cabinets and the interested opposition of local bodies (particularly the treasurers and attorneys to the trusts) to prevent any progress.

Another fortuitous circumstance which shaped highway administration was the growing concern for public health. The connection between sanitation and transportation might seem remote and limited to the circumstance that sewers often lie beneath roads, but by happy accident the first Public Health Act of 1848 made local boards of health, in the newly constituted urban administrative areas, responsible also for the highways (still often unpaved on the outskirts of towns) within their bounds. Those great sanitary innovators, Edwin Chadwick and Southwood Smith, were responsible for the movement away from eighteenth-century squalor which led to a great number of these local boards being constituted, and the important Local Government Act of 1858 ratified their jurisdiction over highways.

This would have been of relatively small significance but for a new Highways Act of 1862 (25 & 26 Vic., c. 61) which gave power to the justices in Quarter Sessions *compulsorily* to combine parishes into highway districts; this was the first element of compulsion and recognized the fact that fewer than a dozen parishes had voluntarily combined under the provisions of the 1835 Act. These highway districts were to function under highway boards made up partly of justices of the peace, *ex officio*, but principally of the waywardens elected by the parishes combined into each district. This left to the vestries only the power to levy rates to meet the demands of the boards, together with the rather hollow privilege of electing their waywarden annually and sending him to act as unpaid assistant to the boards' salaried surveyors, who became the principal figures in the new organizations.

Parochial opposition was furious and the obstructiveness of the parishes was unwittingly strengthened by the failure of the Home Office to guide (or even to inform) the sessional justices in the exercise of this new power.[3] The Home Office, indeed, adopted the attitude which runs like a dark thread through so much of our social and administrative history: the law having been stated, it was not thought incumbent upon anybody to see that it was implemented; not so much as a memorandum of guidance was circulated, therefore muddle, confusion and delay were inevitable and allowed many parishes, rural as well as urban, to creep through a loophole by 'adopting' the Local Government Act of 1858 and constituting themselves into urban sanitary districts and so retaining authority over their roads.

More than 900 parishes, most with fewer than 1,000 inhabitants, thus put themselves in a position to defy the Quarter Sessions simply because a clause in the Highways Act of 1862 provided that no body constituted under the Local Government Act of 1858 was to be included in the new highway districts. It was an obvious abuse of this clause for a parish to constitute itself into a sanitary district *after* the passage of the 1862 Act, expressly to defeat the purpose of that Act, and the Home Office half-heartedly tried to close the loophole by an Amending Act of 1863 which limited the formation of urban sanitary districts to those with not less than 3,000 inhabitants.[4]

In other words the old parochial system was perpetuated under another name; between 1862 and 1882 some 8,500 parishes *were* combined, but in many instances these combinations were only temporary. Those already formed into sanitary districts, together with the older boroughs, retained their autonomy and as late as 1882 over 6,000 parishes still carried on in the eighteenth-century fashion except for the use of statute labour. When it is remembered that even where highway districts had taken over from the parishes there was no common pattern but considerable overlapping of boundaries and consequent internecine strife between one authority and the next, it will be seen that road administration in 1880 was scarcely less chaotic than it had been in 1780. It is true that the wheeled carriage was no longer regarded as a more trespasser on the highways, but the old notion that vehicles must be regulated to suit the roads was implicit in legislation affecting mechanical vehicles (see Chapters 11 and 12).

The balance between a reasonable degree of consolidation for the sake of economy, and the deep-rooted desire to prevent the intervention of any larger authority in local affairs (and the distrust of authority, often justifiable, was, in these matters, illogical), was firmly tilted in the parochial favour. As the 1835 Act had carefully preserved the right of each parish to insist upon the expenditure within its own boundaries of the whole amount of its own highway rate, it is difficult at this distance of time to understand the 'passionate attachment to parochial management . . . in spite of every argument of economy and efficiency in favour of wider administrative units'. The words are those of Sidney and Beatrice Webb and the same authors continue:

How inefficient was the road administration of the Parish even in the middle of the nineteenth century, we can now only dimly picture to ourselves. Only in an infinitesimal number of parishes

did the Vestry dream of appointing a qualified professional expert
as Surveyor of Highways: it would, indeed, seldom have been
easy to secure such a person for the small fragment of his time
that a single parish required. The Surveyors of Highways, it was
deposed as late as 1881, were 'farmers, millers, clergymen, squires'
—when they were not gardeners, bricklayers, broken-down clerks
or shopkeepers, or merely the incompetent relations of prominent
parishioners . . . each parish seems to have thought that its own
highways could not possibly be so well managed as they were
when the parishioners themselves saw to the repairs of their own
roads—that they would certainly cost more because it was vainly
imagined that the local farmers would lend their carts free of
charge . . . that to pay a District Surveyor of Highways [their
moiety of] a salary of £200 a year was more extravagant than
letting a score of parish surveyors . . . £10 or £20 salary for
their amateur work. Above all there seems to be rooted distrust
of the parishes at the other end of the district! This became
intense after the Highways and Locomotives Act of 1878, which
. . . incidentally made a common fund for each Highway District,
replenished by a common Highway Rate, instead of each parish
being financially separate. Who could be sure that an unfair proportion to the common Highway Fund, and an undue share of the
District Surveyor's time, was not being given to the parishes a
dozen miles away, where the soil was soft, the traffic heavy, and
so on? . . . After nearly half a century of advocacy of Highway
Districts, and nearly twenty years experience of them, witness
after witness before the House of Lords Select Committee on the
Highways Acts, in 1881, argued and pleaded, almost passionately,
for a reversion to parochial management.[5]

Another factor which encouraged the retention of parochial
management was that the beginning of the period of 'advocacy and
experience' of highway districts coincided with the start of the decline
of through traffic. By the middle of the century, broadly speaking,
only local traffic remained on the roads, and therefore the localized
patchwork of highway administration was given a new lease of life
which would not have been allowed to it had the stage-coach and the
post-chaise not received their railways-delivered mortal blow during
the reign of King William IV.

This same 'calamity of railways', as Sir James McAdam called it, killed the turnpike trusts; but it was a very slow death. After the successful vesting of the South Wales turnpikes in the county road boards it was proposed to deal similarly with the English and Scottish trusts, and a General Roads Bill was drafted which would have placed both parish and turnpike roads under control of the counties. This measure was instigated by Sir George Grey, the Home Secretary (all parliamentary action connected with roads was the business of the Home Office until 1872), whose Parliamentary Under-Secretary wrote in 1849: 'The . . . Bill was met by the opposition of the Clerks to Trusts, who are nearly all attorneys, and their influence with members . . . was irresistible. We were forced to withdraw it . . .'[6]

Between their most profitable year of 1837 and 1850 the turnpike receipts dropped by one-third, and the most prosperous trusts began to join the shabby ranks of the near-insolvent ones in yielding their falling incomes to their creditors. The major part of their revenues had always come from passenger traffic, but despite initial dislike and fear of the railways few people were going to pay 6d. a mile or more to travel at ten miles an hour in a stage coach when they could travel three times as fast for a third of the cost and have greater comfort and safety into the bargain. In the heyday of the coach and turnpike era each stage-coach paid nearly £7 a year in tolls for each mile it covered; therefore a coach travelling daily between London and Manchester would have contributed £1,700 a year to the trusts *en route*. In present-day values this represents approximately £20,000 a year, so the severity of the 'calamity of railways' is easily judged and the efficiency and prosperity of the coaching industry may be gauged by its ability to carry so monstrous a burden. It needs no discernment to see why travelling, except on foot, was a luxury denied to nine-tenths of the populace before the railway age.

So firmly entrenched was the system, however, that as the revenues dwindled Parliament bolstered up the trusts by giving power to justices in Special Sessions to order a contribution from the highway rate for repair of a turnpike road where the trust's income was insufficient. This was in 1841 (4 & 5 Vic., c. 59), when toll receipts were already dwindling, but expedients such as these could do no more than delay the process. By 1858, when the last regular stage-coach left Manchester for Derby, the turnpike bonds, once a

gilt-edged security, were virtually worthless, and it became each
year less defensible to try to give an appearance of animation to the
moribund body. Victorian parliaments in general might be pusil-
lanimous about reforming highway law, but they could not ignore
facts as plain as these.

A Select Committee of the House of Commons (one of many)
inquired into turnpikes in 1864, but where nearly all previous committees had been concerned to improve, and thus to maintain the
trusts, this one concerned itself with the best means of getting rid of
tolls. The 'disturnpiked' roads of South Wales were now practically
toll-free; Ireland had been entirely toll-free since 1858, but England
and Scotland lagged behind. The committee reported that the
abolition of the trusts would be 'both beneficial and expedient', and
that the best course would be to follow the South Wales precedent.

This report suffered the fate of most Select Committee recommendations; the Cabinet ignored it and the Home Office made no
attempt to formulate a policy, but the feelings of the individual
Members were now definitely ranged against the *status quo*. Successive House of Commons committees gradually hammered out a
policy, and from 1874 onwards a special Committee on Turnpike
Trust Bills was appointed annually and took over from the Home
Office the business of dealing with applications for renewal, and
replaced by strict scrutiny the perfunctory examination and nearly
automatic renewal of Turnpike Acts which had characterized Home
Office procedure for more than a century. Under the energetic
guidance of Lord George Cavendish, M.P., who presided for many
years, this Committee usually recommended against renewal and in
default of any governmental policy the House invariably accepted
the recommendations. When the committee started its work 854
trusts existed; ten years later only 184 were left and 113 of these
were extinguished during the next two years. By 1890 only two
turnpike trusts were left, and fifteen days after Sir David Salomons
organized the first public display of motor cars in England, on 15
October 1895, the last toll was levied on the last piece of turnpike
road in the country—the Anglesey portion of Telford's Shrewsbury
to Holyhead road.

The gradual abolition of the turnpikes went hand in hand with
the undermining of parochial control; a small trust administering
only a few miles might have its road transferred to a 'highway

6 Steam tar-spreader at work at Staines, May 1907

7 Woodblock paviours at work in Farringdon Street, c. 1885

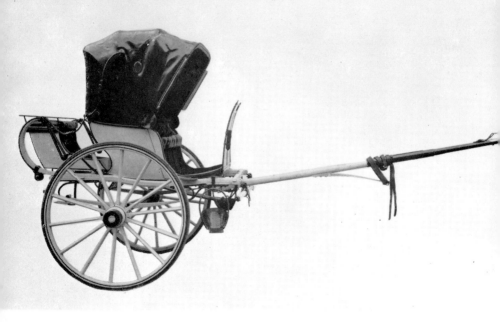

8 Undersprings, cee-springs and elbow springs cushion the ride of the curricle of c. 1830

9 Dished wheels of mid-eighteenth century child's waggon

parish', but in most instances the 'disturnpiked' roads were handed over to highway districts or the urban or rural sanitary districts. Another dent was made in parochial armour in 1872 when governmental responsibility, such as it was, for highway law and administration was transferred from the Home Office to the new Local Government Board created by the Public Health Act of 1872. This board was also responsible for Health and Poor Law administration, and although it became an instrument of Government in highway matters it was not in any sense a Government highway department or ministry. Therefore from 1872 until the creation of the Ministry of Transport in 1919 Great Britain enjoyed, if that is the word, a Gilbertian situation in which no minister was answerable to Parliament for anything directly connected with road-building, administration or finance, although the amount of public money spent on the roads by the end of the nineteenth century was as great as that spent on public education. Parliamentary questions consequently could only be put as supplementaries to other issues, and governmental policy on highway matters could only be exercised indirectly. An example of this is seen in the Locomotives on Highways Act of 1896, which did not, as most motor historians aver, set the speed limit at 12 m.p.h., but at 14 m.p.h. or 'such lesser pace as the Local Government Board may direct'. The initiative, therefore, was left with the board and it was the board which set the lower limit.

The Public Health Act (35 & 36 Vic., c. 79), in addition to creating the board, parcelled England and Wales into urban and rural sanitary authorities, responsible for roads, the former made up of the boroughs and urban districts and the latter roughly following the boundaries of the Poor Law unions outside the urban areas. The first Highways Act passed under the auspices of the board, The Highways and Locomotives Act of 1878, directed that the highway districts authorized in future by Quarter Sessions must coincide with the sanitary districts, but there was still a great deal of confusion about boundaries and functions.

This same Act struck a further blow at the parishes by abolishing parochial separateness in highway finance—their rates had to be added to the common fund on which they might draw, but although the county 'highway districts' had dwindled to 357 by 1894, there were still over 6,000 'highway parishes' struggling to administer their roads on the system laid down in 1555. A great increase in through traffic, the growing popularity of the bicycle, the first rumblings of motor traffic and plain common sense all combined against them. The Local Government Act of 1888 made sweeping changes, particularly by setting up the county councils much as we have them today, and by making provision for help with county expenditure by grants-in-aid from the Exchequer.

The new county councils were made responsible for maintaining all 'main' roads in their counties, though it was left to them to determine which should be 'mained'; it was also left to their discretion to decide by how much, if at all, they would subsidize the repair of the secondary roads which were left in the hands of boroughs, urban districts, rural districts or parishes. In general the parishes thought it better voluntarily to surrender their powers rather than wait to be starved into surrender; the number still functioning as highway authorities dwindled from 6,454 in 1894 to 1,169 by 1897. The end of Queen Victoria's reign brought the end of the chapter.

This is not to say that all was now for the best in the best of all possible worlds. The standard of road maintenance improved greatly throughout the nineteenth century, but still left much to be desired; the rapid growth of motor traffic brought to light fundamental shortcomings in the surfaces which had suited horse traffic well enough (see Chapter 4), and the attempts to rectify these shortcomings revealed that the administrative machine was still cranky and inadequate to deal with the needs of the new users of the roads.

We must now briefly trace the legislation affecting mechanical vehicles, as this necessarily affected road administration. The experimental steam carriages or omnibuses of King William IV's reign attracted no special legislation; they fell within the scope of the laws dealing with ordinary carriages, and when one reflects that some of them weighed between three and five tons, were capable of occasional bursts of speed above 20 m.p.h. and were very inadequately braked by twentieth-century standards it is clear that Parliament would have been justified in enacting regulations to control them. This was made unnecessary by a coincidence; the period of greatest steamcoach activity chanced to coincide with the expiry of a large number of Turnpike Acts, and in their applications for renewal the trusts concerned (all violently anti-steam) asked for, and were granted, power to impose tolls of such magnitude on mechanical vehicles that their chances of commercial success were ruined. The technical men had been hampered enough by lack of financial support, but these new tolls were crippling and tilted the scale towards the railways which increasingly drew capital and engineering talent away from all other forms of transport.

Some revival of interest in road-steamers became manifest in the late 1850s, the bias being now towards slow-moving engines for drawing heavy loads or for agricultural work (though there were a few 'light' steam pleasure carriages), and the Locomotives and Highways Act of 1861 was actually framed to encourage their use by protecting them against excessive tolls. This was follwed in 1865 by the notorious 'Red Flag' Act (28 & 29 Vic., c. 83) which imposed speed limits of 4 m.p.h. in open country and 2 m.p.h. in towns and required all 'road locomotives' to be attended by at least three persons, one of whom was to walk sixty yards ahead of the engine carrying a red flag by day and a red lantern by night. Various other restrictions, such as those governing the use of water from public supplies, were also enacted.

This Act has always been reviled by motor enthusiasts and historians as a prime example of short-sighted governmental interference stifling invention and enterprise, but, as shown in Chapter 11, the Act was not wholly unreasonable in the circumstances of the time. It is, however, fair to say that the next Highways and Locomotives Act, of 1878, which amended and amplified the regulations, was unnecessarily restrictive.

Typical of the pettifogging nature of this Act was the clause which reduced the distance by which the 'Red Flag Man' had to precede a road engine from sixty yards to twenty. Also it was left to the discretion of local authorities as to whether he should carry a flag or not. This was generally interpreted as though the flag was still mandatory, and some of the first private motorists were summonsed for not having a banner borne before them. Henry Hewetson, the English agent for Benz cars, took advantage of the fact that neither the 1865 nor the 1878 Acts specified the size of flag and infuriated the police by having his young son carry before him an inch of red ribbon tied to a pencil.

Whilst these affairs were in progress the bicyclist made his appearance on the roads, and it is difficult now to visualize the vehemence of the hostility aroused by this seemingly harmless innovation. Any protests the cyclist might make about unfair treatment by the police, or neglected roads, were countered by indignant retorts that the 'ironmongery riders', the 'cads on castors', did not even pay rates and consequently were only using the roads on sufferance. It was a step forward in 1888 that it was statutorily declared that the bicycle was a carriage, and so entitled to a place on the roads, even though the bicyclist was obliged to carry a bell (originally required to tinkle continuously whilst the machine was moving) like the leper of old. It was through the agency of the bicyclist that this same statute (51 & 52 Vic., c. 41, s. 85) required all vehicles to carry lights at night: it seems strange to the twentieth-century mind that this had never been enacted before.

By 1888 the bicycle was moving up in the social scale. The advent of the 'safety bicycle' in 1887 and of the pneumatic tyre in the following year made the new transportation fit for women, and the bicycle craze of 1890–5 made it socially acceptable. The bicycle was the most powerful factor in reawakening the idea that roads were of more than mere local concern, and in preparing the way for the acceptance of the motor car. It is notable that all the men concerned in influencing Parliament into drafting and passing the Locomotives on Highways Act of 1896 (61 & 62 Vic., c. 29), which not only raised the speed limit but removed the 'three persons in attendance' rule, were bicyclists or connected with the cycle trade before they became interested in the new horseless carriages.

It was from the growing body of influential motorists that the next impetus was given to reform of highway law, but it was impetus sadly in need of an instrument. The Motor Car Act of 1903 raised the speed limit of 20 m.p.h. and made registration, display of identifying marks and licensing of drivers compulsory; but because of the nature of existing administration it could do nothing towards improving the roads, the inadequacies of which became each day more apparent as more motor vehicles destroyed the surfaces which had been just adequate for horse-drawn vehicles.

For the sad fact became apparent as wails of protest went up from the motorists who had to cope with disintegrating roads, and from those who were choked and blinded by the clouds of dust thrown up as pneumatic tyres sucked up the fine particles which bound the 'macadamed' crust together, that despite all that had been done there were still more than 1,900 different authorities responsible for highways, and that this vast body had no head. The Local Government Board was as supine as the Home Office had been in supervising, guiding and co-ordinating the local authorities; it made no attempt to lay down minimum standards; it did not tell the authorities what they could do, nor did it ask what they had done; it issued no circulars of technical advice and called for no reports; it distributed large sums of money by way of Treasury subvention and audited accounts, but made no inquiry into the state of the roads on which the money was spent; worst of all, because of the peculiar circumstances already mentioned, no minister or government department was responsible to Parliament for the roads.

A Departmental Committee of 1903 illuminated this deplorable state of affairs, but despite proposals for a system of payment of grants-in-aid which, if adopted, would have reduced the number of authorities responsible for roads to about sixty, nothing was done. The Local Government Board was not prepared to initiate the necessary legislation, and it was left to the good sense of the county and district surveyors (fortunately not a rare quality), and to private bodies such as the Roads Improvement Association and the Automobile Club to plan and execute improvements. The immediate results were experiments with tar-spraying and other means of consolidating road surfaces and abating the dust nuisance which, quite rightly, made the motor-owning minority highly unpopular. It is remarkable not that the roads were so bad, but that they were so good, and it is almost entirely because of unofficial bodies that by 1913 Great Britain could claim to have a greater milage of smooth-surfaced, waterproofed motor roads than any other country.

There was still, however, no such thing as a 'trunk road' in Great Britain and the only notable legislative effort made before 1914 was designed eventually to bring such roads into being. This was brought about largely by Lloyd George during his tenure of office as Chancellor of the Exchequer. The Government still shrank from setting up anything like a National Roads Department or Ministry of Transport; but some action was clearly needed and it was equally clearly unjust that the growing cost of road repair should fall exclusively on the ratepayers, most of whom were not motor-owners. Until 1909, apart from a trifling registration fee, motor cars had been licensed and taxed as carriages, but the Development and Road Improvement Funds Act of 1909 (9 Edw. VII, c. 47) increased the licence duty on motor vehicles and taxed petrol at 3*d*. on the gallon. These new sources brought in about £1,000,000 in the first year, and a new 'Road Board' was set up to apportion the money amongst the county councils exclusively for new and specific road improvements necessitated by the new traffic. The immediate jobs were concerned with strengthening road foundations, straightening, easing gradients, widening and so forth, but power was given for new roads to be constructed.

Under the guidance of Sir George Gibb, the Chairman, this first national road authority did a great deal of good, but as its terms of reference confined the financial help to *new* improvements the lesser local authorities, and ratepayers, felt aggrieved that no help was given towards ordinary repairs and maintenance which had risen sharply in cost as motor traffic increased. This was particularly felt in towns and suburbs where motor buses and lorries proliferated with spectacular speed. Motor-owners, private and commercial, also felt aggrieved that the trunk roads did not materialize. Plans were published, for example, for an urgently needed new road from London to Hounslow, but nothing was done. In this instance the new Road Board must be exonerated from the charge, often justified, of governmental readiness to take the taxpayers' money and reluctance to spend it as promised. The Act specifically enjoined the board to counterbalance fluctuations in the labour market; to hold back on expensive schemes in time of prosperity and to accumulate funds for release in times of unemployment—not directly to employ the workless but to stimulate the economy in general. It so happened that the first years of the board's existence were years of national prosperity, but economists predicted that a slump would follow in 1914–15. The board planned for extensive new road work in those years, but, of course, when the time came there was more urgent work to do.

The irony of the situation was that the low unemployment of 1911–14, which caused the Road Board to hold back, was to some extent occasioned by the booming prosperity of the motor industry.

CHAPTER FOUR

Road Construction

The reader who has persevered so far will have realized that 'road engineering' in the modern sense virtually did not exist in the eighteenth century. Routes were not surveyed, and roads 'just growed' though reasonably accurate measurements had been made and milestones and guide-posts erected since the end of the seventeenth century. The word 'engineer', indeed, still had an almost exclusively military connotation, and it is significant that almost the only scientifically surveyed and engineered roads in the United Kingdom were those built under General Wade's direction in the Highlands after the suppression of the Jacobite Rebellion of 1745. These were the only metalled roads in Scotland at the time of their building, and they were good roads in the sense that they provided about 800 miles of properly laid, drained and surfaced highway, but they were bad roads in that they served no purpose once their military *raison d'être* was no more. They could not promote trade where none existed and their gradients were often unnecessarily steep, so that they did nothing to prevent further depopulation and such local traffic as there was reverted to the ancient trackways.

The eighteenth-century road-maker's equipment consisted of a pick, a shovel, a stout wooden rake, a basket or, occasionally, a wheelbarrow. In addition, some villages maintained a monstrous 'road plough'; this fearsome engine, drawn by eight or more horses, would be furbished up every spring and used to 'restore' the parish highways by ploughing them up and throwing the furrows towards the centre. The furrows were then flattened by harrowing and the roads were supposedly ready for the summer traffic.

Dirt roads such as these obviously became useless from waterlogging very quickly, and as England is a wet country they were generally more or less waterlogged. The favourite expedient, provided on the most-used routes, was to lay a causeway some two to four feet wide along the centre of the road or near to one side of it. This paved way was usually raised above the general road level, and as the wheeled vehicle was still regarded as an interloper many parishes separated the 'causey' from the soft road by a line of posts. Where these were not used, and if the difference in level allowed it, carters would get their carts astride the causeway so that their beasts could benefit from the firm going. This led to fights with horsemen and leaders of pack-teams; indeed, fisticuffs were often exchanged between pack-teamsters travelling in opposite directions, as the causeways were usually too narrow to permit of one team passing the other—someone had to take to the mud.

The mud was of a muddiness undreamt of today; it was by no means uncommon to see horses floundering belly-deep after a rainy spell, and this state of things was not confined to remote country districts. The *Gentleman's Magazine* for March 1756 records that the Mile End Road, only a mile east of Aldgate, 'resembled a stagnant lake of deep mud . . . hard work for four horses pulling a light chaise to go faster than a foot pace. . . .'

Where suitable stone was within reach it was used in abundance, sometimes in superabundance, but to little effect, and one of the strictures John McAdam passed on the roads in those areas where stone was readily available was that they were dug quite unnecessarily deep and the resultant trench filled with ungraded stones to a depth of three feet or more, and then topped with gravel, unwashed and adulterated with mud and clay. This system, common in the North of England and almost universal in the Lowlands of (pre-Telford) Scotland aggravated the worst defect of eighteenth-century roads, which was that they absorbed water. McAdam's summing up was that:

> . . . the road is as open as a sieve to receive water, which penetrates through the whole mass, is received and retained in the trench, whence the road is liable to give way in all changes of weather . . . A road formed on such principles has never effectually answered the purpose which the roadmaker should constantly have in view . . . In this kingdom an artificial road is only required to obviate the inconvenience of a very unsettled climate, and water with alternate frost and thaw, are the evils to be guarded against.[1]

The nature of the problem was well understood long before McAdam wrote of it, and the remedies adopted varied from the ingenious to the absurd, but had in common that they succeeded poorly or not at all. The most common expedient was to camber the surface very steeply, so much so that wheeled traffic was seriously incommoded. In some districts this principle was carried to extremes and the road became triangular, apex uppermost, rather than merely curved, the better to shed water on the lines of a house roof. Writing in 1778 John Scott[2] observed that: 'The angle in the pantile roof road is often so great as to endanger overturning on the least collision of carriages, and always enough to occasion anxiety to the timorous passenger.'

Though inconvenient or positively dangerous, the roof-shaped road at least had the merit that it shed the water fairly well, which is more than can be said for the 'road laid wavy', which had a certain vogue in mid-century, particularly in Essex and Leicestershire. The 'road laid wavy' consisted of a series of transverse hillocks regularly spaced along the whole surface of the way, and it was supposed that if workmen were sent with spades, after heavy rain, to let the water out of the troughs the 'bottoming' of the road would remain dry. Arguments as to whether the waves should be short and steep or long and shallow were almost as fierce (and absurd) as those concerning the rival merits of knobs or spikes on lightning conductors; but despite the assertion in the *Gentleman's Magazine* for May 1749 that 'In level countries . . . these waves are absolutely necessary', the wavy road was obsolete by 1780—doubtless to the relief of those obliged to ride in wheeled carriages.

There was also a school of thought obviously swayed by the 'if you can't beat 'em, join 'em principle, and this school used the water to maintain the roads. This resulted in the 'hollow ways' or 'concave roads' so common as by-ways throughout the country. The method was to make the surface slightly concave and by stopping culverts or temporarily diverting streams into the roadway, to wash all the surface mud and debris to the lowest point where men with spades could clear it away. During prolonged rain, of course, the hollow ways became brooks, but where they had fairly good 'bottoming' (usually conspicuous by its absence) this system worked well enough for narrow lanes provided one overlooked the disadvantage that the roadway gradually sank lower and lower between the adjacent fields and hedgerows until, as Edgeworth[3] wrote in 1817: '. . . the stag, the hounds and the huntsman have been known to leap over a loaded waggon in a hollow way without any obstruction from the vehicle'. The hollow ways, now properly waterproofed and no longer concave, are still with us.

The streets of towns were subject to so much wear that a hard, impenetrable paved surface was essential. The terms 'paving' and 'pavement', which now suggest a smooth footpath faced with slabs of real or 'reconstituted' stone, had different connotations two hundred years ago. The 'paved' roadways of eighteenth-century towns would now be miscalled 'cobbled' although, strictly speaking, a cobbled road or path is one faced with smoothly rounded, water-worn shingle-stones, usually flints, disposed in symmetrical rows or patterns, such as survive in Rye and some other seaside towns.

The 'paving' of city streets consisted of blocks of hard stone, usually granite, shaped with the chisel to a more or less rectangular or wedge shaped form. The blocks were anything from six to eighteen inches deep and were shaped with one slightly rounded end which was laid uppermost. The interstices between the stones were packed with earth which, theoretically, soon became so compacted that water could not penetrate. The slightly convex paving-blocks presented a fine, hard-wearing, but far from smooth surface for horses' hoofs and carriage wheels. In many towns, until the century was nearly over, the footpath was not raised above the roadway but formed part of it, being separated from it at busy places by posts: worn-out iron cannon were often used.

The defect of this paving, as commonly executed, was that the stones were not regular either in size or shape; consequently the lateral pressure to compact the earth filling varied, some places remained soft, water penetrated and the paving soon sank and broke up, particularly after frost and thaw. In spite of these defects the paved roads were, at least, rather more durable than most others that our forefathers enjoyed—or endured. In some districts, notably in Lancashire, where industrial traffic was growing and stone was plentiful, even the country roads between towns or villages were paved; but so badly were they laid that they were scarcely less unpleasant to travel over than the ordinary soft roadways. By the end of the century, however, notable improvement had been made to the Lancashire roads.

The clatter of iron-shod hoofs and the ginding of iron-tyred wheels over stone setts is now but a memory, but the din of town traffic is nothing new. During the nineteenth century, and particularly after the coming of the tramways, the methods of paving were improved; stones of regular shape and size, placed upon firm and properly drained foundations and set in hard Roman cement, provided a virtually indestructible surface. So durable, indeed, is properly laid 'pavement', that it is still common on the Continent and not yet extinct in Britain. Those of sufficient years will remember the hazard presented by such roads to the early high-pitched, short wheel-based motor cars, with their smooth-tread narrow-section, high-pressure pneumatic tyres, the gyrations of which upon wet granite setts were at once wonderful and alarming.

The duties of the ancient parish highway authorities did not, generally, extend to building or repairing bridges. As lately as 1773 even the turnpike trusts were legally obliged to do no more than mark the fording places by fixing: '. . . graduated posts denoting the depth of water at the deepest part of the same, and likewise such direction posts or stones as they shall judge to be necessary for guiding travellers in the safest track or passage through such floods or waters'.[4] John Scott observed that these posts: '. . . are a miserable substitute for bridges. In the dark they can be of no use; and in the light they may sometimes induce strangers, depending on the depth specified by the graduations, to ford waters with the strength of whose current they are unacquainted, at the hazard of their lives.'

Where they existed at all, bridges were built and maintained by a great variety of bodies or individuals ranging from the Crown to small charitable foundations and landowners. Money was often bequeathed to parish or county authorities for the building of a bridge and the authority concerned then equally often found it had insufficient funds to keep the bridge in order, and no power to levy a rate for the purpose. The laws governing these matters were, if possible, even more contradictory and confusing than the general highway laws, and the energies of those responsible for maintaining bridges seem principally to have been directed to finding ways to pass the burden to someone else. Many of the old bridges were only wide enough for pedestrians and pack animals, and in 1803 De Quincey wrote:

Even in the nineteenth century, I have known a case in the sequestered district of Egremont in Cumberland, where a post-chaise of the common narrow dimensions was obliged to retrace its route of fourteen miles on coming to a bridge built in some remote age when as yet post-chaises were neither known nor anticipated, and unfortunately too narrow by three or four inches.[5]

As the roads in Scotland were almost universally condemned during the second half of the eighteenth century by all those who had occasion to use them, it is fitting that the two greatest improvers of highways, 'Pontifex Maximus' Telford, the 'Colossus of Roads', and 'McAdam the Magician', were both Scotsmen. The inhabitants of England and Wales, as well as their own countrymen, owed much to them.

The two men were of very different qualities: Thomas Telford was one of the first to qualify for the title of professional civil engineer in the modern sense. He was, indeed, a prime mover in establishing the status of this profession and the first President of the Institution of Civil Engineers; he worked as a practical stonemason; he practised with some success as an architect; he was one of the first engineers to master the technique of using iron on a large scale; his canals were conceived and executed in the grand manner; his road surveying and engineering would not disgrace a twentieth-century team of experts, and the scores of bridges he built (most of which are still in use, carrying traffic far heavier than that for which they were designed) exhibited new modes of design and construction and range from simple single-span stone arches over small streams to such breath-taking masterpieces as Pont Cysyllte and the Menai suspension bridge. By contrast John Loudon McAdam* was no more than an amateur who, by common sense and observation, evolved a method of surfacing roads which was both effective and cheap. Yet it is macadamizing rather than telfordizing which has become part of the language, and in the first quarter of the nineteenth century the influence of the McAdams, father and son, ranged far and wide.

Telford's first works as road-builder were carried out in Scotland, and arose from the efforts of a few conscientious landowners and

* In his lifetime McAdam's name was variously spelt, M'Adam, MacAdam, Macadam and McAdam. The last was the form he usually used himself, whilst the penultimate is the spelling usually given to the type of road named after him.

noblemen who tried to halt the depopulation of the Highlands. The clan system which had held the people of the Western Highlands and Islands together had been broken by the Duke of Cumberland after the rising of 'forty-five', and when the forfeited estates were handed back to the displaced chieftains, or their heirs, in 1787 they betrayed the few remaining crofters by evicting them and turning the crofts into sheep-walks. There were some honourable exceptions, but the rapacity of the clan chieftains accelerated the decline—a decline which, incidentally, is now invariably blamed upon the English Government and people by the Scottish Nationalists.

The Highland Society was formed in 1784 and began to press the Government: two members of Parliament, Henry Beaufoy and George Dempster, were particularly active in this, and two years later, in concert with Lord Pulteney and the Duke of Argyll they founded the British Fisheries Society, as a joint stock-company, to build ports and develop a Scottish fishing industry. Ports were built at Ullapool and Tobermory before the Society's finances were crippled by the slump of 1792, by which time it had become apparent that even without the financial crisis the project would founder for want of internal communications. Government help was essential and Dempster continually pressed the Highland cause in Parliament. He was helped by a report from the Superintendent of Military Roads, Colonel Anstruther, whose graphic description of the disgraceful state of affairs pointed the contrast with the roads in the Lowlands, which had been much improved as a result of industrial expansion there during the last quarter of the eighteenth century.

Despite the pressure of the Napoleonic War, Pitt's Government listened with a sympathetic ear to the Highland plaint and in 1801 the British Fisheries Society, in the person of their engineer, Thomas Telford, was instructed by the Treasury to report on all Highland communications and to recommend measures to stop depopulation.

Telford's first Survey and Report, prepared during the autumn and winter of 1801, between intervals of work on the Ellesmere canal, was shrewd, detailed and masterly. A second report followed in 1803 and earned him the Fellowship of the Royal Society of Edinburgh. His scheme involved not only wholesale road- and bridge-building but extensive harbour works and a canal through the Great Glen to link east and west coasts. As a result of this report two Acts of Parliament were passed setting up a Commission for the

Caledonian Canal, and a second for Highlands Road and Bridges.

Telford was appointed surveyor and engineer to both commissions and the Treasury underwrote the commissions in the necessary money-raising; funds came from Treasury loans, from local authorities and landowners and from the Forfeited Estates Fund.

The road work was split into six divisions, each with a superintendent in charge, but the general direction lay in Telford's hands. During the next eighteen years 920 miles of new road were built, 280 miles of old military road were realigned and resurfaced and had the worst gradients eased, and more than a thousand bridges were designed and built. Many of these, it is true, were little more than culverts, but a number were sizeable and some were grand structures of stone or iron spanning the Spey, the Tay, the Beauly and the Dee. In his stone bridges Telford used a technique he had devised for the Ellesmere Canal aqueducts of using hollow walls for the spandrels of the arches (and, sometimes, for the piers) with internal cross-walls as ties. This gave much greater strength for less material than the old practice of filling hollow walls with rubble.

A thousand-odd miles of road in eighteen years may not seem impressive by twentieth-century standards (though it compares not unfavourably with our progress in motorway construction), but it will be seen as a great undertaking when it is remembered that for most of the time the country was at war and that the work went hand-in-hand with extensive harbour works, with the Caledonian Canal and with the early stages of the Holyhead Road and its bridges. It must also be remembered that many areas of the Highlands were virtually inaccessible until Telford's roads were built, and materials often had to be hauled great distances.

Telford's roads were built to endure, and endure they did. For this reason they proved cheap in the long run, though Telford's contemporaries sometimes accused him of being unduly lavish, and that arch-enemy of progress in general and engineers in particular, Colonel Charles de Laet Waldo Sibthorp, M.P. for Lincoln, sneered at him as 'one of those visionary gentlemen who expects to feed upon the public'. The roads were also, almost for the first time, designed with the wheeled vehicle in mind with gradients and curves made as easy as possible. Great emphasis was placed on the proper grading of the stones and their cleanliness: this is now part of every highway engineer's A B C, but it was a part which had been wholly neglected for centuries. In his Diary, Robert Southey records that Telford's system was:

> First to level and drain; and then to lay a solid pavement of hard stones, the round or broad end downwards; the points are then broken off, and a layer of stones broken to about the size of walnuts, laid over them so that the whole are bound together.

Southey also gives details of Telford's elaborate care over draining (he insisted upon stone-lined drains where they had to pass under the roadway) and the precautions taken on hills, by sloping and turfing, to prevent mud and debris being washed on to the road. He stressed that: '. . . after the foundation has been laid the workmen are charged to throw out every stone which is bigger than a hen's egg.'

Here lies the clue to the durability of Telford's road surfaces. There was, indeed, nothing new in the method which had been practised empirically by some turnpike surveyors and most notably by John Metcalf ('Blind Jack of Knaresborough') in his work for the trusts of Yorkshire, Lancashire, Derbyshire and Cheshire; but in general the eighteenth-century road-makers had used a hugger-mugger mixture of large and small stones and often admitted clay or chalk as a binding medium with disastrous results. As everybody who has tried to make a garden path from odds and ends will know, it is impossible to achieve a smooth hard surface if large stones are mixed with smaller ones, as the former rise to the surface and are kicked or scuffed to one side. Telford's insistence on the use of uniformly sized stone for the foundation and small *broken* stones of irregular shape for the top dressing meant that the grinding action of iron-shod hoofs and wheels, and the attrition of each stone against its neighbours, produced a fine, hard grit which filled the interstices and soon compacted solid so as to be almost impermeable. In combination with a fairly generous camber this surface was sufficiently waterproof to keep the foundation and subsoil dry.

This was also the principle adopted by McAdam, with the significant and daring difference that, for new roads, McAdam omitted the foundations altogether.

John McAdam had spent several years in America and had also travelled in Europe and Scandanavia. He was therefore well acquainted with various road-making methods when he returned to Great Britain and settled in Scotland in 1783. He took an interest in local affairs and soon found himself appointed a Commissioner of Highways; he played an important part in the various road improvements of the industrial areas of the Lowlands; he also made himself acquainted with the whole complex structure of highway administration as well as examining practically every important turnpike road in England, Wales and Scotland. By the time he settled in Bristol early in the nineteenth century he was well informed both in theory and practice and well able to judge different materials and methods. He became a magistrate and, again, a Commissioner of Highways. In 1816 he was appointed Highway Surveyor and was also consulted by the local turnpike trustees. One has the impression that McAdam was something of a know-it-all and that the appointment was given, in part at least, in the hope that he might stop haranguing his fellow justices upon the shortcomings of the existing roads. He soon showed that his practical abilities matched his loquacity; the roads under his care were soon so much improved, at so small a cost, that the word spread and McAdam and his son were in demand by turnpike trusts up and down the country. Before 1820 the words 'macadamize' and 'macadamite' had passed into the language; at one time the McAdams had more than 300 sub-surveyors working to their directions for different trusts, and in 1824 Miss Mitford wrote (*Our Village*): 'We shall see no more of the Surveyor of Highways, for the macadam ways are warranted not to wear out.'

McAdam postulated that provided the road surface was made waterproof by the attrition and compaction of properly graded stone, a thickness of six to ten inches would suffice and the natural soil would carry any weight likely to pass over it. Most of his work was concerned with remaking existing roads, but where new stretches were laid to McAdam's plan they were found to answer very well. He went so far, indeed, as to say that the type of surface he favoured would wear better if laid over a morass than if it were laid on a rock foundation. He instanced a stretch of his road near Bridgwater in Somerset which was partly over ground so soft that, he said, 'When you ride in a carriage along the road, you see the water tremble in the ditches on either side', and partly over limestone rock: his accounts showed that the maintenance costs were as five to seven in favour of the road on the soft ground.

McAdam's theory was discredited towards and after the end of last century, but recent developments have made it once again acceptable. It is, however, important to say that McAdam was as insistent as Telford upon proper draining, and upon the need to ensure that the lowest point of the roadway stood three to four inches above maximum water level in the ditches. Like Telford, too, he advocated placing the side ditches between field and hedgerow, with suitable communicating channels, rather than directly at the roadside. This course was unacceptable to farmers and landowners.

When possible McAdam liked to 'make a road in three times' as he put it: that is, only some two or three inches of 'metalling' were laid at one time and allowed to consolidate thoroughly before the next layer was put down. During the consolidating process men were regularly sent to rake down the ruts, but to a great extent this and the 'making in three times' were made unnecessary by the action of the heavy rollers which came into use by about 1820. McAdam pointed out that if a road was arched too steeply the object of throwing off the water was met at the expense of concentrating all the wheeled traffic, and hence the wear, on the crown. He recommended a gentle curve rising only three inches in an eighteen-foot width.

Because McAdam's method was so successful he was not only in demand by turnpike trusts but was a prominent figure in public discussions on road-making and administration, and he gave evidence before the many Parliamentary Committees on Highways. He also wrote several papers and letters on the subject, and his observations, together with reprints of some of the evidence before Parliament, were published in book form under the title of *Remarks on the Present System of Road Making*; this was an admirable guide both to the practical and the financial aspects which was published in 1818 and had run through three editions by 1820.

The work throws a great deal of light on the financial and administrative difficulties which arose, as McAdam points out, not from fraud but from ineptitude, from lack of scientific observation, from there being too many trusts each controlling an uneconomic length of road and from obsolete laws and customs. He points out that most of the roads round London were particularly bad and that this badness arose very largely from the use of gravel from the Middlesex pits, which was too large and mixed with stiff clayey loam which was very difficult to remove. Excellent gravel had been raised from the bed of the Thames since 1808, when steam dredgers were put to work, but this gravel was denied to the road-makers as the Ballast Act gave Trinity House a pre-emptive right to all ballast materials brought into the Thames. Surplus ballast, much of it suitable for road surfacing, was taken to sea and dumped. Similarly, various Navigation Acts imposed crippling duties on stone brought by coasting vessels, and on the inland waterways; although the cartage of manure was, in effect, subsidized, road materials were penalized by the scale of dues authorized by Parliament.

Much of McAdam's fame rested on the economy of his system and on the employment it gave to women, children and men too old and feeble for heavy work. In the remaking of old roads he would have the surface and foundation raised by stout labourers with pick-axes, and the heavy work of relaying (or of making a new stretch) would also be done by fit men, but he demonstrated that the task of preparing the material, old or new, to his specification needed little strength or skill. He insisted on the use of small, light hammers and made the unheard-of innovation of having his stone-breakers sit at their work. Thus economy and philanthropy went hand in hand, and by the standards of the time the stone-breaking work was light and easy. Where Telford's superintendents used ring-gauges for checking the stone grading McAdam had his sub-surveyors carry a pocket balance and a six ounce weight; he reckoned that the difference in density between one sort of stone and another did not materially affect the size of his 'six-ounce pebbles'.

McAdam reckoned that where no new material was needed a road could be lifted, drained and relaid according to his specification for 1s. per running yard, or £88 a mile for an eighteen-foot width. The price for new materials naturally varied from district to district, but he showed repeatedly that so much stone was wastefully used on the usual run of roads that an admirable job of remaking could often be done, not only without buying more but actually leaving a supply available for future repairs. At the other end of the scale an eighteen-foot width of road paved with granite setts, at London prices, cost about £920 a mile, and the project mooted in 1818 for laying a double-track railway, for horse-traction, from the new East India Docks to the City was estimated at £4,500 a mile.

Where the traffic was particularly heavy, as on this East India Dock Road and similar thoroughfares, the trusts and other bodies concerned often adopted a compromise by paving the centre of the road, to a width of some twelve feet, with granite setts and leaving the remainder 'macadamed'. This system was used for most of the new wide roads built between 1820 and 1860 in the expanding industrial areas of South London and in new suburban developments in such places as Islington, Highgate and so forth, as well as in many provincial towns. It was a reasonable enough compromise by the standards of the time; heavily laden wagons monopolized the paved strip, leaving the sides to faster and lighter traffic. Unfortunately this type of road remained in use long after it was outmoded. It had always been a source of complaint that the paved section was often at a higher level than the rest, presenting awkward bumps up and down to crossing traffic, and when the first tramways, with their projecting rails, were laid along the paved strips the complaints became so loud, and so justified, that sunken grooved rails were substituted. By the time the motor car became well established these dual-surfaced roads were generally better levelled and the unpaved portions were asphalted or 'tarmacadamed', but the sudden change from one type of surface to another added greatly to the hazard of the 'dreaded side slip' from which the pioneer motorists suffered. The hazards were increased still further by those municipal authorities who electrified their tramways by erecting a line of standard-posts down the centre of the roadway to support the overhead wires for both lines of track. This ensured that the only safe method of passing a tram was on the near side, which zealous constables pounced upon as illegal.

The paving of nineteenth-century roads was much better than that of the eighteenth; the folly of using odd-sized tapering blocks was appreciated and it was seen to be important that stones of regular shape and size should be laid, like brickwork, in 'courses', so that the joint between one block and its neighbour came midway between joints in the adjoining rows. The addition of lime to the filling, to concrete the joints as water penetrated, became common practice in the 1830s, and before the end of the century hard mortar was used and the foundation properly concreted. Concrete- and mortar-mixing machines, driven by steam or internal-combustion engines, began to be used before 1914 for major works; but for minor operations and repairs the concrete mixing was still done by hand.

Paved roadways, properly laid and bedded in concrete, provided the most durable of all surfaces. So durable that it went against the conscience of the finance committee or highways department to authorize their removal until quite recently. Their durability was also a drawback when sections of road had to be lifted to allow pipes or conduits to be installed or repaired. This was not a matter which the eighteenth-century road-makers were often obliged to consider, but one of the first fruits of the industrial revolution was the cast-iron water pipe; this led to rapid development of piped water supplies which had formerly been limited by the expense of lead pipes or the inability of elm pipes to remain leakproof for long. Better water supplies naturally led to the adoption of water-borne sanitation and a corresponding increase in underground sewers and connecting drains. In 1811 the first short length of street in London was lit by coal-gas and the Gas, Light and Coke Company was formed in the following year. The new gas lights sprouted everywhere, first in the streets, then in public buildings and finally in private houses; this meant more pipes below town streets and by the 1880s telephone and electricity cables began to join the below-ground labyrinth. Inevitably, all these developments entailed expense and inconvenience, as roads had continually to be taken up and relaid in order to install or repair pipes and cables.

There were those who criticized McAdam for being a mere copyist, and it is true that his method of surfacing had been used not only by Telford but by Rennie, over his bridges, by Abercromby in Scotland and by Pierre Trésaguet in France. It was his energy and his careful analysis of the financial and social aspects of road-making which won McAdam so wide a following and earned him the title of 'McAdam the Magician'. Sir Henry Parnell[6] was one of those who pointed out that he had introduced nothing new, but, with justice, said of him that he '. . . certainly had the merit, of no inconsiderable value, of being the first person who succeeded in persuading the Trustees of turn-pike roads to set seriously about the improvement of them . . . he produced a considerable change for the better in all the roads in the Kingdom'. This was certainly true, and Parliament recognized the nation's debt to McAdam by making him a grant of £10,000: in 1834 he was offered a knighthood, which he asked should be granted to his son. He died in 1836, and Thomas Telford followed him in the next year; the two men most responsible for making possible the wonderful regularity and speed of the mail- and stage-coach services consequently died just as the railway fever was about to become hectic.

It would be wrong to assume that road improvement stopped altogether with the coming of the railway age, but it is true that the impetus went out of the business to a great degree and new methods of construction were almost wholly confined to urban streets. Private and commercial vehicles of all kinds grew in number, but through traffic virtually vanished from the roads between the 1850s and the 1880s, when a few energetic bicyclists began to make excursions on their exhilarating but unwieldy 'ordinaries'. At the same time the steam traction engine emerged as a commercial proposition, and showed up weaknesses in those 'macadamed' roads which had little or no foundation. John McAdam himself had reckoned that four to five tons carried on four wheels would be the most that his roads would have to bear, and when, half a century after his death, they were asked to carry twice or thrice that burden they sometimes gave way. Neglect as well as overweight contributed to those mishaps which left a traction engine stranded with its wheels sunk through the crust and its underbelly firmly aground. McAdam's contention that a smooth waterproof surface, ten to twelve inches thick, resting directly on the soil would suffice has been proved again in recent years; but the roads newly made or remade towards the end of the last century were, in effect, telfordized rather than macadamized, though the latter name was still used.

The really destructive element was not so much the heavy steel-shod traction engine with its train of heavy steel-shod wagons but the light swift motor car. Telford, McAdam and the rest had relied upon the pulverizing action of slow-turning, large-diameter, iron-tyred wheels to fill the interstices, but the sucking action of smaller, fast-turning pneumatic-tyred wheels drew out the binding medium. As motor traffic increased the dust cloud raised by each car on a dry day not only brought curses down upon the head of its owner, but was an outward sign that the road surface was being destroyed.

The water-cart with its sprinkler bar across the back had long been a familiar sight, and its gentle spray had sufficed (for an hour or two) to 'lay the dust' in the pre-motor era; but attempts to solve the dust problem of the motor age by watering the roads were comparable with Mrs Partington's valiant efforts with her mop.

Apart from watering, the first proposals for abating the dust were

concerned with devices to attach to the car. This was partly a reversion to the eighteenth-century principle of adapting the traffic to
suit the roads, but principally a reflection of the motorists' own
concern to suppress the nuisance. This was not wholly altruistic,
however, as a good deal of the dust was drawn into the car and penetrated every crevice of the ankle-length dust coats, veils, face masks,
and scarves with which the occupants sought to protect themselves.
A popular accessory was a large iron-framed canvas dust screen to be
attached behind the back seat in the hope that the eddies it created
would prevent the dust cloud being drawn into the car by the back-
draught of its passage.

This was only to preserve the occupants, but other 'dust pre-
venters' were supposed to prevent the dust cloud from forming. They
mostly took the form of shields and deflectors of one kind or another,
but a lunatic fringe of inventors produced a rich crop of improbable
devices which were seen in all their glorious absurdity at the Royal
Automobile Club's Anti-Dust Trials of 1908 and similar occasions.
These fantasies ranged from mechanically driven brushes to sweep
a dust-free path in front of the car wheel, to bell-mouthed suction
pipes behind each wheel to draw the dust into a gargantuan vacuum
cleaner driven from the gearbox.

It was obvious that, for a given speed, some vehicles raised more
dust than others, and the greatest promise seemed to lie in the
direction of making the under-works free from projections to create
eddies. The Dutch Spyker car, which had a smoothly contoured
undershield running the full length of the chassis, earned the title
of the Dustless Spyker, but although such shields helped to prevent
the dust rising they did nothing to stop its formation and the only
real solution was to prevent the creation of the dust by sealing the
road surface.

The impetus came from private bodies, such as the motor clubs
and the Road Improvement Society, rather than from the highway
authorities. Spraying with oil was tried, chiefly on short stretches of
road temporarily closed for speed trials or rallies, though with little
success; but for some time the application of calcium (in one of its
many forms) was widely favoured. The calcium was carefully watered
and the resultant lime formed a crust over the road which was effective, but not durable enough: it soon became clear that some form of
pitch or tar held out the best hope.

The use of tar as a dressing was of respectable antiquity, for as early as 1838 a stretch of Oxford Street had been paved with wooden blocks set in, and made waterproof by, a thick dressing of hot pitch. This type of paving soon became popular, particularly in fashionable residential districts where its quietness was appreciated, and the growth of the gas industry helped by making large quantities of coal-tar available at by-product prices. If the top dressing was allowed to wear too thin, a wood-block road might suddenly disintegrate in patches during heavy rain because of the blocks swelling, but provided it was re-tarred regularly it was a surprisingly durable form of pavement—too long-lived, indeed, for the comfort of those motorists who found it unpredictably slippery in some conditions of slight rain.

The first experiments with coal-tar as a top dressing for ordinary 'macadamed' roads were done in a small way, with the tar heated in wheeled 'tar boilers' and poured over the surface from ordinary watering-cans fitted with suitably coarse 'roses'. This messy and inefficient method was still used by many councils for repair work until quite recently. It soon became obvious that the horse-drawn tar boiler could easily be made into a mobile sprayer by fitting it with a sprinkler bar connected to the tank, but the essential finishing coat of granite or limestone chips was done by hand and shovel—and often ill done if one is to believe the vociferous complaints of those who found the varnish of their cars or carriages spattered with tar.

Although no single government department supervised road planning or construction, it would be unjust to ignore the work done at the National Physical Laboratory to establish the best form of motor road. This work is particularly associated with Colonel R. E. B. Crompton, who may be called a real pioneer motorist, as it was he who organized the 'road train' services in India using Thompson steamers which he had modified for the purpose.

Under Crompton's guidance the N.P.L. experimented with a variety of road-making and surfacing methods and equipment. They used a 'road machine' he had devised to determine the resistance of different surfaces to compression, impact and abrasion. The published results of his experiments influenced road-surfacing techniques to the extent that Crompton has been called the McAdam of the motor road.

Many different varieties of coal- and wood-tar or natural petroleum products were tried, including such 'proprietary' mixtures as 'West-rumite'. The best-known natural tar was that obtained from the famous asphalt lake in Trinidad. The great merit of all these substances was that they could easily be made liquid enough to penetrate the top surface of a road to make, as they hardened, a completely dust-free, waterproof and reasonably durable crust. Only rarely does the temperature in Great Britain rise high enough to soften tarred roads, but it soon became apparent that although a 'tarred macadam' road was good a 'tarmacadam' one was better. The second, and much more durable, process consists in mixing an amalgam of road metal with hot tar and spreading it over the road foundation, to a thickness of some four to six inches. This has to be done whilst the amalgam remains plastic, and the process was, indeed, quite widely practised in towns before the motor car made it desirable elsewhere. The Corporation of the City of London, and many other urban authorities had 'asphalted' some main thoroughfares (on top of the existing stone setts very often) during the last three decades of Queen Victoria's reign and the resultant billiard-table smoothness, though very slippery when wet, was warmly welcomed by those accustomed to rattling and jolting over the 'cobblestones'. As used at first, this 'asphalt' was an amalgam of tar with finely ground limestone, almost reduced to the smallness of sand, but in the new century the contractors who specialized in this work developed different textures of material, varying from McAdam-style 'six-ounce pebbles' to sharp sand according to the nature of surface specified. The coarse-textured stuff was better suited to motor traffic than the ultra-smooth. Whether coarse or fine, or the common combination of a coarse base and a rather finer top-dressing, all forms of 'tarmacadam' (soon abbreviated to 'tarmac') had to be spread and levelled while hot and this called for skilled teamwork. The only part of the business which was mechanized to any extent before the Great War was the final consolidation, after cooling, with the invaluable steam-roller which had been introduced as a commercial proposition in the 1880s. The work of the power-driven mixers and spreaders with which we are now familiar was performed by men with shovels and heavy, wide rakes, who had to be as agile as they were muscular. The actual mixing of the 'metal' was usually done at roadside depots, set up for the purpose, and some contractors toyed with steam-driven mixers; but back-breaking spade-work was chiefly relied on. The gargantuan hooded blow-torches on wheels which are now used to keep one section of the newly laid metal soft in readiness for the next layer were not known, and large shallow fire baskets on small wheels, filled with blazing coke, were used instead. Rather similar fire baskets were carried on the iron-sheathed, low-wheeled, horse-drawn flat trucks which brought the hot material to the site; these helped to keep the prepared amalgam from cooling too quickly and were also used to heat the workmen's shovels, rakes and rammers.

Though lacking the economy and efficiency of today's methods, the making of a 'tarmac' road provided a fascinating spectacle; particularly if seen towards dusk, with drifting tar-scented smoke obscuring the flickering fires, the panting steam-roller and the sweating workmen who leaped and barrowed and shovelled and levelled and raked the heavy, glutinous, obstinate stuff as easily, it seemed, as they spread the dripping on their bread.

McAdam had postulated that 'A road ought to be considered as an artificial flooring forming a strong, smooth, solid surface, which should be at once capable of carrying great weights, and over which carriages may pass without meeting any impediment'.[7] The smoothness was never achieved by the ordinary process of macadaming, nor would it have suited the horse, however agreeable for the occupants of the carriage, but the 'tarmac' surface exactly met McAdam's original specification. The cost was considerable, but the amount of money spent on the roads had been increasing very much for some twenty years before the advent of the motor car. The increase in population and trade had sharpened the need for better roads, many miles of highway were rebottomed and improved in the 1880s and the coming of the bicycle brought about further improvement.

As the bicycle was relatively cheap, and in its early form only usable by the young and athletic, those who sat in places of power, local and national, had at first despised those who 'rode ironmongery' and ignored their complaints. After the introduction of the pneumatic-tyred 'safety' the bicycle quickly became fashionable; influential people began to join the 'cads on castors' and fresh impetus was given to road improvement. It is not possible to assess how much the bicycle craze (or any other single factor) affected development, but it is not insignificant that the total expenditure on roads in England and Wales (excluding those administered by London and the County Boroughs for which the figures are higher) increased by

85 per cent between 1890 and 1902.[8] This represents an annual increase of over 7 per cent (during a time of stable prices), which is nearly three times the average annual increase during the previous two decades and rather more, indeed, than for the years between 1902 and 1910, when motor traffic was beginning to take effect.

The attitude of authority in general, whether at parliamentary or parish level, to motor traffic was discouraging to the point of obstructiveness. Whilst motor-owning remained the prerogative of a few, the many who paid the rates, from whence came the only revenue to make and mend roads, were loud in their condemnation of a system which apparently charged the pleasures of the rich upon them. Although the newspapers of the time carried numerous letters of protest from 'Ratepayer', 'Citizen', 'Paterfamilias' and our old friend 'Pro Bono Publico', the injustice was not really as grave as it seemed. In its infancy the motor car *was* the rich man's plaything or the enthusiast's hobby-horse, but within a remarkably short while it became part of the middle-class *zeitgeist*—and the middle class paid the rates.

Consequently we are faced with the paradox that the country which was more restrictive in its attitude to the motor car than any of its European neighbours except Switzerland, spent more money on its roads immediately before the Great War than any other: even the United States apparently spent less.

The Road Board which was set up in 1909 increased motor licence duties and imposed a fuel tax to raise funds for *new* road improvements, and in 1913 £18,000,000 were devoted to reconstruction and maintenance, though the dream of new trunk roads remained a dream. The white roads of Britain were steadily turning black as the carefully steam-rolled crushed granite or basalt 'tarmac' spread; but although the surfaces grew better and better, the twists and turns, the constant changes of width, the sudden changes from one texture to another and the total lack of co-ordination were still conspicuous. Some efforts were made to ease the worst blind corners, but authority was usually content to deal with bad gradients by exhibiting notices exhorting drivers to 'slacken bearing rein whilst ascending'. The Royal Automobile Club, the Automobile Association, the Motor Union and the Cyclists' Touring Club exhibited notices warning of dangerous hills, deep fords or other hazards, but the signposts, speed-limit signs and other 'official' directions were still (as they often are yet) fixed by the highway authorities at heights convenient for the drivers of stage-coaches.

The steam-roller had become a fairly common tool by 1910, but was by no means universal, and one of the considerations which induced the Tynwald to permit the Automobile Club to stage the Gordon Bennett Race Eliminating Trials, and then the Tourist Trophy Races, in the Isle of Man was the gift of a steam-roller. Mechanical diggers and earth-movers, mostly steam driven, began to be used, but as, generally, they were not self-moving but had to be mounted on lengths of wide-gauge railway track alongside the work, they could only be economically employed on large projects. Steam diggers and mechanical concrete mixers were used on a large scale to good effect in the construction of the racing track at Brooklands. This was a private venture, planned and financed by Mr and Mrs Locke King, which was of inestimable value to the motor industry. Although the concrete roadway of the Brooklands track soon became notoriously bumpy (because of being put to use, it is believed, too soon after the concrete was poured), its remarkably speedy construction showed what could be done with concrete if the scale of the operation was big enough to justify mechanization.

Public roads made wholly of concrete did not materialize, except experimentally, until after the war, but more and more road authorities, particularly the urban ones, were adopting the principle of a concrete base below a 'tarmac' top. It was easily foreseen, and cogently argued by Lord Montagu of Beaulieu and other notabilities in the motor world, that new trunk roads would soon be urgently necessary. For the reasons outlined in Chapter 3 nothing was done before the war. Road construction had come a long way since the days of Telford and McAdam, but road constriction was as bad as ever.

Book Two

The Vehicles

CHAPTER FIVE

Wheels, Axles and Tyres

At first sight the cart wheel, and its lighter cousin the carriage wheel, seem simple enough structures, and so they may once have been, but as experience grew the wheel became a more and more subtly complex affair, beautifully adapted to its purpose by the gradually developing skills acquired by generations of wheelwrights and smiths. At the core of the craft lay that instinctive knowledge of timber which the wheelwright shared with the boat-builder and cabinet-maker. These craftsmen, often illiterate, could judge un-felled timber and when the tree was brought to the sawpit could determine, before the planks were cut, which part of the tree would be suited to a particular purpose. This not only made the best use of natural curves and forms but economized labour; the wheelwright also had to develop an uncanny accuracy of eye, for the different parts of a wheel had to be made to very close tolerances; yet until the end of the nineteenth century most wheelwrights used no machinery beyond a crude pole-lathe, and few measuring instruments beyond a large pair of 'outside' calipers, a foot-rule and a piece of chalk.

We do not know the name of the unsung genius who first hit upon the idea of 'dishing' a wheel, thereby increasing its lateral strength whilst reducing its weight, and it is most likely that the principle was discovered accidentally. If this is so, it was a happy accident, and it appears to have happened during the second half of the sixteenth century.

A flat-spoked wheel, without 'dish', lacks lateral strength unless it is very heavily constructed. This was a grave drawback in the days when deeply rutted roads called for large-diameter wheels: in order to withstand side-thrust the spokes had to be far thicker than was necessary to carry the vertical loads, and naves and felloes had to be increased in proportion.

The lateral strain on cart and carriage wheels was largely exerted

69

inwards, tending to push the periphery of the wheel towards the centre-line of the vehicle. This force was particularly exerted on the outside wheels whilst cornering, and the opposite force, which tended to push the rims of the inside wheels outwards, was of little consequence at hippomobile speeds. Steeply cambered roads and deep ruts added to the inward side-thrust, but even when running straight upon a smooth flat surface the wheels were constantly subjected to similar side-thrust, acting first on one side and then on the other, because of the motion of the horse or horses. Those who can remember the sounds made by a horse-drawn cart on a quiet country road will recall that in addition to the clop of the hoofs, the jingle of harness and the grinding scrunch of steel tyres there was a continual undertone—clink-clunk, clink-clunk. The 'clink' was made as a slight outward force carried the wheel out against washers and linch-pin, and the heavier 'clunk' resulted from the far greater inward thrust as the whole weight of the vehicle and its load was delivered against the inside of the nave. Even at walking pace this battering-ram effect was considerable, and the dished wheel running on suitably canted axles provided a very neat engineering solution.

The dished wheels provided the further advantages that they made it possible to increase the width and carrying capacity of coach or wagon body, as the sides could be canted outwards to match the cant of the wheels; the dished wheels also tended to throw mud away from the vehicle and not on to it, and the dishing also imparted a little resilience to the wheel structure (particularly when hoop tyres came into use), which lengthened its life by helping to keep the joints tight.

On the old Yorkshire principle that 'you don't get owt for nowt' all these benefits were bought at the cost of a serious drawback. In order that the wheel should not 'run on its toes', but that the whole width of the tyre should bear on the road, it was necessary to bevel the outer circumference of the felloes to correspond with the degree of dish of the wheel and the angle of the axle end. In other words, the bearing surface of the wheel became conical instead of cylindrical.

If it is left to its own devices a conical wheel tends to run in a circle; therefore if it is forced to travel in a straight line (or turned in a direction contrary to its natural inclination) some part of the area in contact with the road must skid instead of rolling. This sliding friction obviously must damage the road, wear out the tyre and waste power by increasing the rolling resistance.

With wheels of normal dimensions these disadvantages were less serious in practice than in theory, particularly as no road surface was truly flat. A light carriage wheel with a two-inch tyre usually had about ten to fifteen degrees of dish, and its rolling resistance would scarcely be affected, but a perceptible amount of scuffing would take place with a two-wheel dray or dung-cart carried on four- to five-inch wheels dished about twenty to twenty-five degrees. Unfortunately the legislature stepped in, as it so often does, to make the matter worse. It was obvious that a wheel too narrow for its load on soft ground sunk more deeply than a wider one, and the turnpike trustees were given power to fix their tolls in relation to a combination of gross weight and tyre width in such a way that the construction of wheels of grotesquely exaggerated width was encouraged.

The theory had something to commend it, but in practice the results were thoroughly bad and, as always with bad legislation, the system remained in use for many years after its weaknesses had been amply proven. The scale of charges was so adjusted that it became virtually mandatory to use broad-wheel wagons for heavy loads, and the charge for 'overweight' was so severe that the wheels were, indeed, made even larger than the Act specified. On the largest broad-wheel wagons, which scaled eight tons gross, the wheels had to be not less than nine inches wide, so arranged as to roll a sixteen-inch path at each side of the vehicle. As so pronounced a 'crab track' would have been very inconvenient, wheels of twelve to fourteen inches in width were used for such juggernauts.

As the only method of road maintenance and repair practised in the eighteenth century was to cover soft patches, and fill ruts and holes with broken stone, leaving it to be rammed, ground and rolled into place by the hoofs and wheels of traffic, the idea of making every goods vehicle into a road roller appears not unreasonable. Nor would it have been, apart from expense and inconvenience in construction, if the broad wheels had been cylindrical and upright, but as the inherent difficulties of making and hanging them make it essential that they should be steeply dished, their peripheries had to be conical. The damage and the waste of power caused by dragging these conical rollers over and through the roads were prodigious.[1]

In order to reduce the drag the wheelwrights tried to defeat the intention of the Turnpike Acts whilst observing the letter by making the wheel rims not truly conical but spherical. Though the curvature of a twelve-inch wheel rim might be so slight as to be imperceptible to the eye, it nevertheless reduced the actual bearing surface (on a hard level road) to little more than three inches—sufficient, indeed, had the deception been acknowledged, to incur an 'overweight' toll on an eight-ton wagon of no less than forty pounds at every gate—but this still entailed a lot of wasteful scuffing and grinding on ordinary surfaces. On paved or cobbled streets of towns the grinding and pulverizing effects of broad wheels were also very destructive; particularly because it became the accepted practice for the strake irons, or sectional tyres, to be fixed with large nails with projecting domed heads about the size of half walnuts. The reason for this is not apparent; on all other forms of wheel the strake nails were countersunk and the surface smooth, but the broad-wheel wagons always had these projecting lumps which acted like hammers as the wheels went round.

The broad-wheel wagons were an unmitigated nuisance. The biggest of them needed at least eight horses, usually worked with ten and frequently required twelve. This meant that each horse pulled a net load of only twelve to sixteen hundredweight, which is about half the load which a good horse is capable of pulling in a properly designed four-wheeled cart. With the steering lock restricted by the clumsy wheels, and with ten or more horses, the big broad-wheel wagons made the finest traffic-stoppers in narrow streets that the wit of man could devise. Yet they were not quite extinct by the 1820s, but still lumbered about, serving as mobile monuments to legislative folly.

Elm, oak and ash were the wheelwright's principal materials, and the axe, the adze, the chisel and the plane (or 'shave') his principal tools. Elm made the best material for naves, or stocks as they were often called, ash was used for felloes (always pronounced and often spelt 'fellies') and 'John Oak made the spoke'—at least until the end of the nineteenth century, when imported American hickory spokes were sometimes used for light work. Conscientious wheelwrights insisted upon using cleft oak saplings for spokes, and they were so shaped that the heart wood made the rounded back portion, which did the most work, leaving the softer sapwood to be prettily shaped to a knife-edge with the spokeshave. Spokes made from sawn timber from mature trees did not last so well: a properly made wheel might serve for thirty years, and when it could be re-tyred no more the spokes would be cut down for smaller wheels or for barrows. When these wheels in turn wore out the spokes were sold to ladder makers and reshaped into 'rounds'.

Nearly all the shaping of the felloes was done with the axe, leaving but little to be finished with the drawshave, and in many country wheelwrights' shops the naves, too, were used as the axe left them, though for any but the heaviest carts and wagons a turned finish was essential. It is important to remember that the provincial wheelwrights, so called, made complete vehicles as well as making and repairing wheels.

The nave having been shaped, bored to take the 'axle box' and marked out with caliper and chalk, the mortises were cut. These had to be accurately dimensioned so that the spokes fitted tightly, and accurately sloped so that the spokes assumed the calculated angle of 'dish'. The roughly finished spokes were driven home with a heavy maul, cut to length (the ends having been battered over in the driving process) and the ends shaped into square or, more generally, circular dowels which were then sawn to take the tightening wedges. The felloes, one to each pair of spokes, were then marked and bored to fit on the spokes, and drilled at the joints to take dowel pegs: the very greatest nicety in this drilling was essential, because, of course, as the felloes were hammered on to the spokes the diameter of the complete ring decreased and the dimensions had to be so judged that as each felloe reached the shoulder on each spoke the adjacent felloe joints closed together without gaps. The spoke wedges, heart of oak, were then driven home; the outer rim of the felloes was then finished with axe and drawshave and the ringed wheel was ready for the tyring smith.

The next part of the business involved joint efforts by wheelwright, smith and helpers, as speed was essential. Most etymologists say the English spelling of 'tyre' is incorrect and the older form, 'tire', now regarded as American, is more appropriate because the word derives, they say, from 'attire'. As the one-piece hoop tyre was a comparatively, late invention, and wheels were originally 'attired' or shod with curved plates or strakes the argument seems valid. In the eighteenth century, however, although 'tire' was the usual form, one occasionally comes across 'tyer' and in the sense that the metal cladding not only provided a tough wearing surface but 'tyed' the wheel together it may be that the modern English spelling is correct.

Even the old strake tyres played an important part in consolidating the structure; they were so proportioned that each felloe joint came in the centre of a strake plate. Having been heated and curved on the anvil to the correct radius, the strake was heated again and tapering holes were punched through it. When cool the strake was then 'offered up' to the wheel and corresponding holes marked and drilled through the felloe, slightly offset from the corresponding strake holes in such a way that the act of beating in the nails tended to draw adjacent felloes together. This was helped by a screw device called a samson which hooked under one of the nails, left slightly projecting for the purpose, at one end, whilst its movable bridge piece was passed round a spoke and firmly bolted home. This had to be done without loss of time, because, for its final placing, the strake had again been raised to red heat, together with the large nails (about the size and shape of sardines), and the whole job of anchoring the strake at one end with a nail driven right home, the placing and tightening of the samson, and the insertion of the remaining nails (ten to a strake usually) had to be done before the wood caught fire. As the last nail went home one of the helpers swung the wheel round (it was mounted vertically on a false axle) so as to quench the strake in a suitable water trough. The contraction of the iron completed the job of pulling the felloe joint tight. The process was then repeated on the opposite side of the wheel, and so on until all the strakes were in place. Tyres for broad-wheel wagons were made up of four, five or six rows of strakes side by side.

The welded one-piece hoop tyre was even more efficient at 'tying' the wheel, as it not only pulled the felloe joints together but forced the spokes home in the mortises: if the degree of shrinkage had been correctly judged the red-hot tyre as it cooled also gave a slight curvature to the spokes and so prolonged the life of the wheel by making it resilient. The earliest hoop tyres were made of such a size as to be a tight fit when knocked on to the wheel cold; the all-important improvement of making them undersize, expanding them in the fire and relying on their shrinkage to secure them and strengthen the wheel is attributed to James Hunt, who was awarded a sixty-guinea prize for the application of this principle in 1769. The business called for great accuracy of eye and hand on the part of the smith, who had to apportion the length of the bar before scarfing the ends, rolling it to its hoop form and 'shutting' the scarfed ends together to ensure that as the tyre contracted, after being finally heated and knocked into place, the shrinkage was enough to make a firm long-lasting wheel, but not so much as to strain the spokes by putting too much 'bow' in them.

The matter was further complicated because for all but the lightest and narrowest wheels the tyre, having been 'cut and shut' into its circular form, had then to be bevelled, by stretching one edge with hammer and fuller, so as to suit the coned outer circumference of the wheel. This work not only required skill but strength: a four and a half inch tyre for a dung-cart, for instance, was made from a bar five-eighths of an inch thick, and material enough to embrace a four foot eight inch cart wheel meant that the smith and his hammer man had to juggle with more than a hundredweight of red-hot iron.

Although the hoop tyre came into use quite early in the eighteenth century, heavy country carts and wagons were still shod with strakes until the end of the nineteenth century. No doubt, at first, many country wheelwrights and their tyring smiths lacked the necessary bending rolls, and transport problems made it difficult to get the requisite lengths of bar delivered in remote places. When all these difficulties had been overcome the innate conservatism of all craft industries still perpetuated the use of strake tyres.

Apart from final touches with drawshave and glass-paper in readiness for painting, the wheel was now complete except for the important business of fitting the 'axle box', or hub bearing in twentieth-century language, adjusting it until the wheel ran true and shrinking on the hoops at front and back of the nave. For ordinary carts and coaches these hoops were of painted iron, but for private carriages they were 'close-plated' with brass or silver.

On the earliest coaches, and on ordinary carts until surprisingly late, the entire axle tree was of wood, including the tapered extremities on which the wheels revolved. These axle ends were sheathed with iron to reduce friction, but they were necessarily of large diameter, which entailed having large, clumsy wheel naves. From the mid-eighteenth century onwards all but the cruder country-made vehicles had iron axle ends, supplied complete with 'boxes' from the foundries of Birmingham, Wolverhampton and

Lambeth, ready to be bolted to the wooden axle trees which now became axle beds or ex beds. Complete forged iron axle trees came into use in the last years of the eighteenth century.

The common iron axle box was made in two halves, welded together with the seams left 'proud' to help locate the box in the nave: before being joined the two halves had depressions hammered into them to retain grease. In a mistaken attempt to correct the drag of conical wheels the axle ends and boxes were tapered, and each end of the box was flanged, the inner end to work against the 'shoulder collar' on the axle and the outer end to work against suitable washers interposed between the end of the nave and the linch-pin, which went through a slot in the outer end of the axle to hold the wheel in place.

No attempt was made at accurate centring and boring of the nave in order to locate the axle box concentrically with the wheel rim. The hole was deliberately made oversize and the box loosely inserted; the wheel was then mounted on a false axle end attached to the workman's bench and revolved against a gauge block on the floor; oak wedges were then driven into the nave until the wheel ran true in both planes. These wedges also served to lock the box into the nave, and as they could not be removed once they were driven home, great judgement was needed to make a wheel true by this crude but effective method.

In addition to being canted downwards to correspond with the degree of 'dish' of the wheel, the axle arms were set pointing slightly forwards. This 'foreway', as it was called, served much the same purpose as the 'toe-in' of the front wheels of a motor car, and was also supposed to ensure that the end-thrust was taken against the shoulder collar rather than the linch-pin.

The 'common axle box', as it came to be called after the introduction of improved types, had many shortcomings, yet continued to be fitted to commercial and farm vehicles into the present century. One defect was that iron upon iron provides a bad combination for frictional contact and does not wear well; lubrication was needed at intervals of a hundred miles or less and the only sure way of greasing the common axle box properly was by taking the wheel off. The most serious weakness lay in the method of fastening by a flattened iron linch-pin passed through a rectangular slot in the end of the axle. Despite the 'foreway' a certain amount of end-thrust came on the pin and the fretting of the washers between pin and nave, which increased with wear, enlarged the slot and made it difficult to keep the pin from rocking to and fro, and finally jumping out (despite the safety-pin which could also shake free) or breaking. 'Wheel off' was a common accident, inconvenient enough on a slow wagon or cart, but not infrequently fatal on a faster vehicle.

Patented and improved axles and boxes, 'oil axles', 'anti-attrition axles', 'safety axle boxes' and 'self-lubricating wheel boxes' began to make their appearance in the last decade of the eighteenth century. Two types predominated, the 'Mail' and the 'Collinge'; both became so well known, the latter particularly, that they lost their capital letters and the thirteenth edition of the *Encyclopaedia Britannica* (1914) merely says of axle arms and boxes: 'They are of two kinds, the "mail" and the "collinge".'

The mail axle, so called because the G.P.O. insisted that the mail-coach contractors should use no other, was patented by John Besant in 1795. The box or journal part was of chilled cast iron accurately fitted to spin on a parallel axle arm which was grooved for oil distribution. The shoulder collar was welded to the axle and before welding a loose-fitting but stout flange was placed behind it: from three holes drilled in this flange long bolts passed right through the nave, which was retained with suitable nuts and washers. A face plate or thrust washer and a leather oil retainer were interposed between the shoulder collar and the nave, and the outer end of the box was enlarged into an annular oil reservoir with a smaller recess turned on the inner end: a brass plate screwed to the front of the nave enclosed the whole affair, and an oil tube with a screwed plug allowed the reservoir to be filled without dismantling the wheel. Unless the flange behind the shoulder collar wore completely through or all three studs failed the wheel could not come off accidentally.[2]

Collinge's patent was not unlike the mail axle in that both relied on oil passing from front to back of the box, but the main oil reservoir on the Collinge took the form of a large hollow cap screwed over the end of the box. An annular recess formed the inner reservoir, and the usual steel face plate and leather retaining washer went between the nave and the shoulder collar; the centre of the axle arm was reduced slightly in diameter for an inch of its length to form another oil pocket. The principal novelty of the Collinge axle lay in the use of nuts, with left- and right-hand threads, to retain the wheel; in other words, it was a product of the machine age, as the nuts had to be accurate and interchangeable.

The outer end of the Collinge axle arm was reduced in diameter in two steps with the clockwise and anti-clockwise threads turned upon them. The outer end of the axle box was made with a conical rebate and an accurately ground conical-faced collet was slipped upon the axle arm to work against this: the part of the arm on which the collet sat had a 'flat' ground upon it and a corresponding 'flat' in the collet prevented the latter from turning. The collet was then screwed up to a working clearance from the box by a large bronze nut, followed by a smaller nut locked against it by the reversed action of the threads. As the collet could not revolve, no turning effort came upon the firmly locked nuts, but as a further precaution the outer extremity of the arm was drilled to take a split pin.[3] Threaded axle ends with securing nuts, in addition to the linch-pins, were sometimes used in conjunction with 'common axle boxes' from towards the end of the eighteenth century onwards; but these were coarse-pitched hand-rolled threads and did not allow for interchangeable nuts and accurate fitting as the patent improved wheel boxes did.

The Collinge axle was as safe as the mail, but the wheels were more readily removed if necessary. The oil was fed from the outer end to the inner partly by capilliary attraction and partly by the pumping action of the collet which had a slight lateral movement in rhythm with the alternating end float of the wheel. Mason's improvement to the Collinge box, which soon became standard practice, consisted of casting lateral oil channels in the box itself and doing away with the reduced section in the middle of the arm. Further improvement came with the use of gun-metal or hard phosphor bronze for the box in place of iron.

The deservedly high reputation of Collinge axles and boxes rested partly on the design and very largely upon the very high standard of accuracy and material. The axles were 'faggoted' in the manner of gun barrels; that is, they were formed from several flat bars forge-welded into a solid mass, whereas cheaper quality axles were made of square bars formed between rollers. Each Collinge box was lapped in on the arm for which it was intended, and where a common axle box needed greasing every hundred miles or so, and the mail axles would run for two or three weeks without attention (though the

G.P.O. insisted on their contractors inspecting and lubricating wheels each day), a Collinge axle was good for 5,000 miles without attention.

Roller bearings were often proposed and occasionally used from about 1830 onwards, but the advantages they offered were not sufficient to justify the difficulty and expense of making them. Cup-and-cone ball bearings of the bicycle type were sometimes fitted to very light pony traps and similar vehicles at the end of the last century, but in general ball and roller wheel bearings belong to the motor era.

The skill of wheelwright and tyring smith were the most important factors in wheel-making, and as early as 1837, in his treatise on carriage-building, William Bridges Adams wrote:[4]

There is no remedy for this evil [bad workmanship] except substituting machines for men's hands. All the machinery should be worked by a steam engine . . . every piece of wood in a wheel ought to be shaped by machinery; the machine if it cuts true once will cut true always . . . that wheels continue to be made by hand in England is a somewhat remarkable thing. There is scarcely an article of manufacture for which there is so large a demand, and there is no variation in their mode of construction.

There may have been no variation in the mode, but there was enough variation in wheel sizes to make the installation of steam power and repetition machinery unprofitable; and inertia, craft conservatism and trade unions also played a part in opposing mechanization. By the end of the nineteenth century machine-made spokes and naves were fairly extensively used, but on the whole wheelwrighting remained a handicraft.

This meant that the strength and durability of each wheel differed from the next, and even the best workman could turn out bad work under the influence of ill health, a change in the light (so much being judged by eye) or a hangover. Because, generally speaking, only the best workmanship has survived we are too apt to assume that all the craftsmanship of the past was good; but poor work and shoddy materials were as prevalent a hundred and more years ago as they are today. As roads improved and the vehicles upon them proliferated the proportion of faulty wheels to perfect ones increased.

As we have seen, a good wheel might run for thirty years or more, but it was not unknown for a poor one to collapse in thirty days. One has but to dip anywhere in the Post Office archives to find evidence. The three following extracts are typical:

Sept. 21st. 1796 . . . the near fore wheel of the Newmarket coach, and both fore wheels of the Ipswich broke this morning. I must beg you will order your people to pay particular attention to the wheels . . .

Oct. 24th. 1796 To Mr Baker, Foreman the Mail Coach Manufactory, Millbank. Dear Sir, In consequence of the off fore wheel of the Ipswich coach breaking this morning and the Guard being unacquainted with his discipline . . .

Nov. 21st. 1796 . . . the down coach, No. 33, was left at Rochester last night with the off hind wheel broke . . . Exeter [Mail Coach was] changed at Salisbury after wheel broke. Shrewsbury ditto. Oxford ditto . . .

So the melancholy records continue. Stage-coaches and other vehicles, not being so rigorously inspected and overhauled as the mails, suffered even more wheel trouble. Improved road surfaces lessened the hazard only slightly, as higher speeds exacted their toll and wheel failure remained the commonest cause of roadside breakdown. Inventors turned their attention to the problem and many patents, some sound and some scatterbrained, for improved wheels were filed during the first half of the nineteenth century. Few of these inventions saw the light of day and fewer still survived.

Of all these inventions that of Walter Hancock was one of the most important: the Hancock wedge wheel was specifically designed for use on his steam omnibuses as wheel failure proved to be one of the greatest hazards which faced the steam-carriage speculators of the 1820s and 1830s. Because of the difficulty of running driven wheels on canted axles, the steam-coach wheels had to be made without 'dish'; this robbed them of some lateral strength and necessitated very heavy spokes, but a far greater difficulty lay in the weakness of the conventional structure when asked to transmit torque from nave to rim. Hancock's solution was to abolish the conventional nave altogether and to make the spoke roots into wedges instead of tenons; each wedge abutted upon its neighbours so that the whole assembly made a strong barrel-arch. The ends of the spoke roots were sufficiently cut back to admit the axle box, and two stout circular metal flanges (usually iron castings, but sometimes bronze) were applied front and back and secured by bolts passing through the

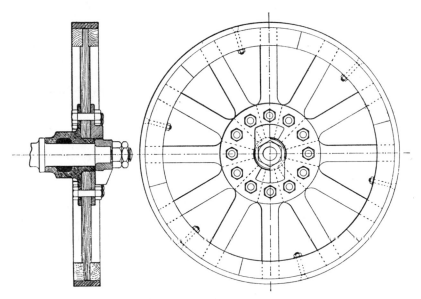

Figure 1 Hancock's wedge wheel: forerunner of the twentieth-century motor car wheel

spokes. This form of wheel was admirably strong, both vertically and laterally, and a turning effort delivered at its centre was transmitted to the periphery through all the spokes, whereas the conventional wheel, when used as a driver, virtually delivered the load upon each individual spoke in succession.[5]

Apart from its virtues as a driving-wheel for self-propelled vehicles the Hancock wheel was so much stronger, weight for weight, than the conventional sort that it was adopted for gun carriages, limbers, ammunition carts and similar very heavy work; consequently later generations knew it as the 'artillery' wheel and the inventor's name was largely forgotten. Some thirty years after Hancock had devised his wheel a similar mode of construction was adopted by the

McNeile brothers, who founded the Patent Steam Wheel and Axle Company. Their products were excellent, but they claimed the 'artillery' wheel as their own invention. The Hancock was the commonest form of motor-car wheel used during the first twenty years of this century, and some American cars were still being equipped with wood-spoked artillery wheels as late as 1932, a century after their first appearance.

The Warner wheel of 1884 was widely used; it was less sound in principle than the Hancock wheel, but a considerable improvement upon the conventional kind. Malleable iron was substituted for wood in the nave, and the spoke mortises were accurately machined on the dividing plate rather than being judged by the eye and hand of the wheelwright.

Another form of new wheel which came into its own many years after it was invented was the suspension wheel, or wire wheel as it is now known. The older name derives from the fact that the weight is hung from the uppermost spokes, which are in tension, rather than pressing on the lowest spokes in compression and it is remarkable that this type of wheel was first designed for a flying-machine rather than for a land vehicle. In the course of his experiments with ornithopters Sir George Cayley designed and caused to be made very light wheels on the pyramidal suspension principle in 1808: the spokes were made of tightly stretched cord with the intention that their elasticity should provide shock absorption on landing. Although Sir George's ornithopter did not fulfil its inventor's aspirations, the suspension wheels were completely satisfactory, and Sir George Cayley had similar wheels made for barrows and light hand-carts for use on his estate.

Theodore Jones re-invented the suspension wheel for railway use in 1831, using iron rods in place of the cords. Each spoke was provided with a threaded portion and an adjusting nut at the inner end where it passed through a suitable anchorage in the cast-iron nave, and although these wheels failed at railway speeds, because the spokes stretched, worked loose and broke, similar wheels were used with some success on light carts and hand-trucks. The suspension wheel did not really come into its own until the coming of the bicycle era. As a power transmitter the radial-spoked wire wheel was not wholly satisfactory, but by arranging the spokes tangentially this shortcoming was obviated and that universal genius Dr Frederick

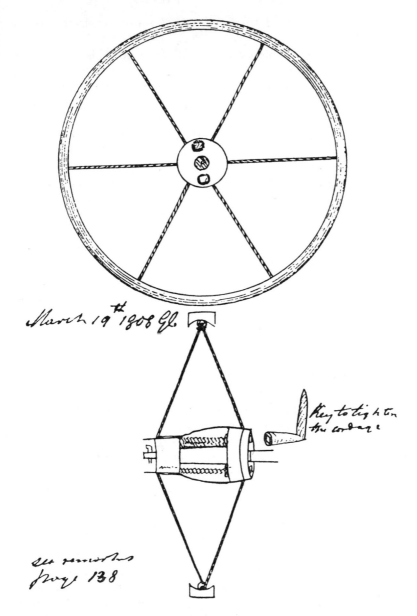

Figure 2 Sir George Cayley's drawing of his suspension wheel from his
Notebook

Lanchester transformed the cycle wheel into a satisfactory motor wheel in 1895.

The vagaries of fashion and its influence on design are amply illustrated by the history of the wire wheel. Despite Lanchester it was regarded with suspicion in this country during the first years of this century: at one period, for example, certain models of De Dion Bouton were sold with wire wheels in France but had to be supplied with artillery wheels for sale in England. This prejudice being overcome, the wire wheel became *de rigeur* for fast and expensive cars, until, in the 1920s, solid disc wheels became fashionable, whereupon many cars with wire wheels were fitted with dummy discs of sheet iron. Now the wheel of fashion has turned again; pressed steel disc wheels are almost universal, but those who seek to be in the swim have their disc wheels diguised as wire wheels.

In the eighteenth century coaches and other sprung vehicles had the springs interposed between body and 'carriage', that being the name given to what, in motor-vehicle terms, is now called the 'chassis'. Early in the nineteenth century new designs provided for additional springs to be placed between the axles and the carriage part; these were known as 'underspring carriages', and ultimately it was found advantageous, particularly for light vehicles, to abolish the separate suspension of the body, to incorporate the 'carriage', the perch and underframing, with the body frame and to rely entirely on the 'undersprings'. Engineers had for a long time pointed out the advantage of applying the spring as near to the source of concussion as possible, and this led to a crop of designs for 'elastic wheels'.

Apart from limited success with spring wheels on heavy, slow-speed traction engines towards the end of the century it must be said that the spring wheel proved almost as much of an *ignis fatuus* as the philosopher's stone. The invention and re-invention of different types of spring wheel continued into the motor era, when the frailty and expense of pneumatic tyres provided inventors with reason to seek an alternative; even C. S. Rolls of Rolls-Royce backed the Hallé spring wheel until an extended trial proved its lack of worth. In an attempt to avoid the complication of the pneumatic tyre many of the devices proposed merely substituted a different sort of complication, and one variety of spring wheel for cars contained over six hundred parts and weighed more than a hundredweight and a half.

Nevertheless, the idea of providing some elastic medium at the point of concussion was perfectly sound and many attempts at cushioning, with rope, leather and similar materials, were tried in the early nineteenth century. Robert Thompson was granted a patent in December 1845 for a pneumatic tyre with an inner air tube or multiple concentric air-sacs of rubberized calico enclosed in a bolted-on casing of canvas and leather. A few broughams, including his own, were fitted with these tyres by Whitehurst and Co., to whom a licence was granted. May and Jacobs of Guildford also obtained a licence and supplied tyres to the Duke of Northumberland, but the world was not ready for the pneumatic tyre and the venture did not pay. In 1846 Thompson experimented with solid bands of indiarubber encircling flanged wheel rims. A few carriages were fitted with these elastic tyres, but they were expensive and troublesome; rather more success (which brought the inventor no profit) was achieved on hand barrows for railway porters and similar light work. The difficulty was that the method of hardening rubber by 'vulcanization' (discovered by Charles Goodyear of Connecticut in 1839) was still in the experimental stage and the rubber Thompson used was apt to be too soft and was liable to become tacky in hot weather.

Some twenty years later Thompson designed a 'light' three-wheeled steam tractor (it weighed about five tons) which was intended for drawing special omnibus trailers or goods wagons. Amongst the novel features was an indiarubber tyre, some five inches thick and twelve inches wide, which represents the first attempt to use a resilient tyre on so large and heavy a self-propelled vehicle.

The Thompson solid tyre was a flat continuous band which was stretched on to the rim, a detachable flange being bolted on afterwards, but as it contained no inextensible bracing wires (as later solid tyres did), and was fairly soft it soon stretched. Consequently all the while the engine worked the soft rubber tyres worked slowly backwards round the advancing wheels, and the rate of wear was rapid. In wet weather, or when working on muddy ground, the 'creep' of the tyres could become so pronounced that the vehicle stood still whilst the driving wheels revolved inside the tyres. Thompson accordingly designed an armour of steel plates or shoes to fit loosely over the tyre, pivoted on stout pins attached to the wheel flanges; these took the driving torque and protected the rubber, but soon were ground to pieces by mud and dust. The armoured rubber tyres were, indeed, very troublesome and expensive, but nevertheless a considerable number of rubber-shod Thompson tractors were made in the 1870s; they could not be used profitably in England, but proved their worth in Egypt, Greece, Turkey and India.

Just as the suspension wheel was brought to perfection for bicycle use, so was the solid rubber tyre. Better methods of fixing and improved vulcanization techniques made it reliable and economical; by 1885 'wired-on' hard rubber tyres were being used for light carriages. In that year the Earl of Shrewsbury and Talbot put a fleet of improved hansom cabs on the London streets; they were built by Forder and had rubber tyres. They were very successful; so much so that people would let several ordinary cabs go by on the chance of being able to take a Talbot, and other cab proprietors, to their annoyance, were obliged to fit the new tyres. The Shrewsbury and Talbot Cab and Noiseless Tyre Company Limited was launched as a public company in June 1888 at almost precisely the same time that J. B. Dunlop fitted his son's tricycle with the pneumatic tyre he had re-invented for the purpose.

Improvements were very quickly made in England, America and France to the first crude Dunlop tyre, and a great deal of litigation over patent rights went on. Some English carriages were fitted with Kingston Welch pneumatics in 1892–3 and in 1894 some of the Paris *fiacres* were fitted with Michelin pneumatics; finally on 11 June 1895 the first pneumatic-tyred automobile took the road. This was a Peugeot which the brothers Michelin entered in the Paris-Bordeaux-Paris-Race in order to prove the usefulness of their tyre for motor-car work. Whilst the tyres consented to hold air they certainly proved their point, but by the time the brothers had exhausted their stock of twenty-two spare inner tubes, and exhausted themselves in so many other roadside repairs that they lost count, there appeared to be some point in Emile Levassor's observation that the air-filled tyre could never be of the slightest use for automobiles.

CHAPTER SIX

Carriage Construction

In the scope of this book it is impossible to give a detailed account of all the different types of vehicle seen on the roads of Great Britain since the middle of the eighteenth century. The list seems endless: coach and chariot, curricle and chaise, cabriolet, clarence, brougham, stanhope, tilbury, denett, dog-cart and drag, berlin, barouche, britzschka and brake, gig and whiskey, sociable and victoria the names roll on from the humble governess cart to the grandiose pilentum, but in many instances the differences between one and another are very small or merely reflect a shift in nomenclature according to period, country or usage. At one time, for instance, a vehicle which was referred to in England as a French chaise was called by the French a *Chariot Anglaise,* and at the beginning of the nineteenth century the English chaise was only so called if it had a box seat for a coachman and was arranged to be drawn by one horse; if it was adapted for two-horse traction it became a chariot or coupé (it was, indeed, a coach cut in half), but if the coachman's seat was removed and a luggage boot substituted the same vehicle became a post-chaise and was driven by a postillion.

Fortunately the business is less complex than this might make it seem: all two-wheeled vehicles descended from the car or chariot of remote antiquity and all four-wheel passenger carriages trace their descent from the agricultural or timber wagon which is scarcely less ancient.

By the middle of the eighteenth century the name 'coach' (the word and the vehicle are of Hungarian origin) signified a rigid-roofed closed vehicle with two *vis-à-vis* seats to hold four or six passengers, arranged with the body part suspended above the 'carriage' (the name given to what, in motor-car terms would be called the chassis) by leather braces acting, usually, with steel springs to insulate the passengers from the worst of the jolts. Until

87

some early nineteenth-century coachbuilders introduced some fundamental changes in the 'carriage' part, the relationship of all four-
wheeled passenger carriages with the coach was clearly discernible.
Thus, as we have seen, a chariot or coupé was a truncated coach with
one inside seat instead of two, a landau was a coach with collapsible
'heads' which transformed it into an open carriage, a landaulet was
to the landau what the chariot was to the coach and so on.

Until the twentieth century vehicle-building was largely a branch
of woodworking; the metal parts, though highly important, were
subsidiary, and in the finest passenger carriages the craftsmanship
was of the cabinet-making rather than the carpentry order. There
was also a kinship with shipbuilding and the method of marking out
the timbers from the 'cant board', a full-scale projection of the
designer's drawings, was very similar to the method used in boat-
yards; also, the basic element of the 'carriage' was the perch which
may be compared with the keel of a ship. This was the main
longitudinal spine to which the fore and hind axle beds were scarfed.
The hind bed was stayed by 'wings' and 'nunters' which linked the
axle bed to the perch in the manner of radius arms so as to relieve the
scarfed joint of strain and to keep the axle bed at right-angles to the
perch. Similar stays steadied the fore bed beneath which the fore
axle tree was pivoted on the perch bolt.

Attached to the front axle was a rectangular framework of wood,
wood and iron or wholly of iron according to the period and type of
the vehicle. The fore and aft members of this framework, two or
four in number, were called futchells and at their forward ends they
were joined to the splinter bar to which the pole, or shafts, and traces
were attached and by means of which the horses exerted their pull
upon the vehicle. Though agricultural and goods wagons usually had
straight futchells (in two-wheeled carts they formed part of the main
frame), these longitudinal members were often forked at their leading ends in order to spread the load evenly on the splinter bar, and
the name derives from 'fourchill' (fourché–fork). Similarly the
splinter bar was a corruption of 'splint tree', or timber to which the
splints and traces were attached, and until the middle of the nineteenth century some writers clung to the spelling of 'splintre bar'.

The futchells were extended for some distance behind the axle
and their rearward ends were united by a stout curved timber which
rested upon the underside of the perch; this was known as the 'sway

bar' and a similar but shorter member, just ahead of the front axle, also rested on the perch and the function of these pieces was to steady the carriage when the front wheels were 'locked over' and at the same time to relieve the perch bolt of bending stresses. These timber sway bars continued practically unaltered into the twentieth century on agricultural and commercial wagons, but on passenger carriages, by the mid-eighteenth century, a circular (or three-quarter-circular) piece of iron work, the 'hooping piece' was attached to the upper side of the front axle and a similar piece to the under-side of the axle bed. This was known as the 'wheel plate' or 'locking plate' and the well-greased surfaces of the two circular metal members served as a steady-cum-thrust bearing for the forecarriage, relieved the perch bolt of bending strain and worked with much less friction than the old sway bars. The rear cross-piece uniting the futchells retained the name of the sway bar, although the wheel plate had taken over its principal function.

This whole assembly of fore axle, axle irons, futchells, sway bars, hooping piece and splinter bar comprised the forecarriage, and the whole weight of the rest of the carriage, the body and the load were pulled along by the perch bolt; despite a large margin of safety it was not unknown for this to give way, generally when the hind wheels struck some obstacle or deep rut which the front wheels had escaped. Whilst the horses careered away with the forecarriage the rest of the vehicle generally overturned.

The basic 'carriage' or chassis of perch, axle beds and wheels with the framing which constituted the forecarriage was probably first constructed to carry felled timber, which was easily done by attaching vertical standards to the extremities of the beds so that a tree trunk placed above the perch was prevented from rolling sideways against the wheels. To transform the affair into a cart was simply a question of building on a structure of planks attached to the vertical standards, which would then have been canted outwards to make the wagon body wider at top than at bottom. A suitable floor of longitudinal planks or poles would have been fixed to the beds with extra transverse ties as necessary. It is most likely that loads were often carried lashed to poles, themselves lashed to the beds with no further bodywork, and the flexibility of such an arrangement doubtless suggested the first use of spring suspension.

Until the fifteenth century passenger carriages were generally no more than glorified and highly decorated wagons with the bodywork and roof or canopy rigidly attached to the perch and axle beds. Such coach bodies, though sumptuously painted and lined with rich stuffs must have been sadly uncomfortable, as the only insulation from jolts was provided by the stuffing of the cushions. As early as the reign of Richard II, however, there was a vehicle known as the whirlicote, used for carrying royal or noble ladies who were too delicate to ride, which consisted of a hammock slung on the standards of a wagon, and it seems curious that this hammock-type of suspension was not more widely used for some three hundred years.

There are occasional references to suspended vehicles in the fifteenth and sixteenth centuries, but it was not until the early seventeenth century that they became at all common. The suspended coach body, hung by leather braces from the four standard posts, was necessarily shorter than the earlier form of body which occupied almost the full length of the perch, and the essential form of the eighteenth- to nineteenth-century coach, with domed roof and rounded bottom, was well established by 1620. Full-height doors with sliding glasses were adopted by mid-century.

The suspension braces mitigated the discomfort of the ride, and removed some stresses from the body, but imparted a swaying motion very trying to those with delicate stomachs: check straps of various kinds linked body and perch and limited the extent of the swing. The next step was to introduce elastic members into the suspension not only to improve the ride but to overcome the weakness of all-leather suspension straps which often broke under the strain of the constant jolting.

It is unwise to be dogmatic about the first application of steel springs, but the balance of probability is that it was an English contribution to the carriage-makers' art, despite some claims on behalf of a French man-hauled vehicle called a *charette* which was, in effect, a closed rickshaw or wheeled sedan-chair. A patent was granted in 1625 to Edward Knapp, but it is doubtful if any practical steps were taken until later. It is likely that single bars or strips of 'steeled' iron were first used and experience must soon have shown that such a single spring quickly fatigues and breaks. The single wood or steel spring of long-bow or cross-bow does not fatigue, for it is prevented from too much rebound by the bow string, and by the middle of the seventeenth century the 'modern' form of laminated spring had been evolved with additional plates clipped or loosely riveted to the main member to increase resistance on bending and to limit the rebound by friction between the plates. This form of 'leaf' spring, as it is now called, is still extensively used after more than three centuries, and still cannot be improved upon for some purposes, although it has been fashionable for motor-car experts to sneer at it for some time now.

It is not possible to put a name to the first man to hang a coach body on steel springs, but it is clear that some of the most eminent seventeenth-century scientists and amateurs were associated with early experiments. Robert Hooke, having turned his attention to the balance spring for watches and formulated the statement expressing the nature of a spring's reaction *'ut tensio sic vis'*, was among those interested in the problem. Colonel Blunt, or Blount, and Lord Brouncker were also amongst the practical experimenters and Samuel Pepys's *Diary* makes mention several times of 'Tryalls about making of coaches to go easy', and under 5 September 1665 he records: 'After dinner comes Colonel Blunt in his new chariot made with springs . . . and he hath rode he says now, this journey, many miles in it with one horse, and outdrives any horse, and so easy he says. So for curiosity I went in it to try it, and up the hill to the heath, and over the cart ruts, and found it pretty well but not so easy as he pretends.'

Before springs were used the leather braces had been attached to extensions of the 'rockers', as the curved bottom frame members of coach bodies were called, and the first form of spring suspension to be standardized, to some extent, was the substitution of short 'elbow' springs for the rigid extensions of the rockers. These 'elbow' springs roughly corresponded to what are now called quarter-elliptics and they were found useful in a variety of different applications. The next step was to hang the upper ends of the braces from springs rather than from the rigid standards, and in the early form of this type of suspension the springs were similar to modern semi-elliptics, arranged vertically (or nearly so) with the lower end anchored to the axle bed, with clips or bolts securing the centre of the spring to the standard, and with the brace attached by a suitable swinging shackle to the 'eye' formed in the upper extremity of the spring.

With the spring clipped to the standard in this way its lower half did little or no work, and by the middle of the eighteenth century what were known as 'whip' springs were substituted. These were like elongated elbow springs, anchored at their lower ends to suitable triangular blocks secured to the axle beds: this made the whole length of spring, now free-standing, effective, and the rigid standard posts were abolished altogether or reduced to ornamental scrolls. The angle at which the whip springs were placed varied, but it was usually not far removed from the vertical; they generally acted alone, but were sometimes used in conjunction with elbow springs attached to the rockers. Early in the nineteenth century they became more and more curved, finally developing into the C formation which remained in use as long as carriages were built.

By the end of the eighteenth century, also, the long leather braces had been replaced by iron links or shackles with short leather attachments at top and bottom. Little ratchet windlasses called 'jacks', were often fitted to adjust the braces according to load or wear, and improved means of checking the swing of the body were continually being devised.

The practice of carrying more and more passengers and luggage on the roofs of the public coaches—the permitted number finally reached fourteen on stage-coaches—made it increasingly difficult to keep the swaying within reasonable bounds when the body was hung on a combination of springs and braces, and by the start of the nineteenth century the public coaches were mostly mounted on 'telegraph' springs, so called because they were first used on a coach called *The Telegraph*. The arrangement consisted of eight semi-elliptic springs, four to each end of the vehicle. Two springs were attached longitudinally above each axle bed, linked by inverted transverse springs which were bolted at their centres to suitable blocks or 'pillows' below the bodywork.

As the longitudinal and transverse springs were united by inter-laced D-shaped links this suspension was very noisy, but in all other respects it was satisfactory and allowed a reasonably easy ride without too much pitching and rolling. It was adopted with various modifications for private vehicles. One finds, for instance, certain forms of phaeton supported on elbow springs in front and telegraph springs behind. A very common variant of this suspension, used on most hansom cabs during the second half of the last century, had the fore-most cross-spring omitted, leaving the two longitudinal springs pivoted to the body frame at their forward ends, and the single inverted transverse spring shackled to their rear extremities. This three-point mounting was sometimes called 'platform' springing and it was used for the rear suspension of a number of pre-1914 motor cars.

The greatest single improvement in vehicle suspension since steel springs were first used came when springs were directly attached to the axles so that the 'chassis' was spring-mounted as well as the body part. This not only made the motion easier but allowed all the 'carriage' parts to be made much lighter.

This new method coincided with the general adoption of all-iron axle trees, and credit for it is usually given to Obadiah Elliot of Lambeth, who was granted a patent in 1804 for his plan of mounting the bodies (suitably strengthened) of four-wheeled carriages directly upon elliptical springs attached to the axles, dispensing altogether with the perch, cross-beds and other appurtenances. The new full-elliptic springs were sometimes called 'nutcracker' springs. The principle was not new, for very light two-wheeled carts had some-times been made with elbow springs attached to the axles, but Elliot's use of elliptic springs and the abolition of the perch on full-scale carriages was a new departure which allowed carriages to be made much lower as well as considerably lighter.

New designs of carriage on this principle followed one another in quick succession, the only disadvantage being that the grinding of the wheels and the rumble of the wheel-plate, particularly in close carriages, were much more obtrusive than formerly. Partly because of this and partly because of the coachbuilders' (and their customers') resistance to change, the older form of perch carriage continued to be made, but with directly sprung axles in addition to the separate body-suspending springs. To avoid too much resilience these 'underspring' perch carriages, as they were called, had semi-elliptic springs to do the actual work on the axles, but the appearance of a full ellipse was preserved by the use of suitably shaped dumb-irons, which were frequently covered with wood casings carved to resemble the lamina-tions of a leaf spring.

The 'underspring' perch carriage is attributed to Windus of Bishopsgate Street in 1818 and it was developed by the most cele-brated of early nineteenth-century coachbuilders, Samuel Hobson of Long Acre, which, under his influence, became the centre of the London carriage trade. Not only did Hobson refine and improve all the mechanical details of carriage work, but he showed mastery of the aesthetic part of the business in his command of line, proportion and colour. He was responsible for the introduction of wrought iron, in place of timber and iron, for the perches and axle beds and for a great number of refinements to such things as folding heads for landaus and barouches, windows, blinds, concealed door hinges, automatic folding steps and other aids to comfort and convenience. Hobson had learnt his craft as an apprentice to Barker and Company, one of the few firms of eighteenth-century coachbuilders still surviving.

The clarence may be taken as an example of the new trend in design set by the introduction of the 'perchless' vehicle. This carriage was first made to the specification of the Duke of Clarence (later King William IV) in about 1824 by David Davies. It was, in effect, the old coupé or chariot redesigned as a perchless vehicle, with the fore boot and coachman's box seat framed into the body. The back part of the body was cut away so as to keep the wheelbase short by bringing the rear axle and springs underneath the seat: three-quarter-elliptic springs were employed at the back and they were attached to the body by elegantly formed brackets called 'pump handles'. The practice of cutting away the underside of the body to allow the axle to pass beneath the seat was copied on many other nineteenth-century carriages, particularly on Chapman's improved form of Hansom's cabriolet. The most important feature of the clarence was that the whole front panel of the body, from the level of the fore boot to the roof was replaced by a large window. The occupants therefore had much more light than usual and a reasonable view forwards, though, of course, the outlook was rather focused upon the coachman's posterior. A folding occasional or 'cricket' seat was usually fitted below the front window of the clarence, and curved or D-shaped front windows became fashionable.

The four-wheeler or 'growler' cabs were direct descendants of the original clarence; and the first brougham, built by Robinson of Mount Street for Lord Brougham in 1839, was a clarence in miniature with the body part only four feet long from front to back. This allowed just comfortable room for two; but the original one-horse 'pillbox' brougham soon grew up into a bigger affair, the double or D-front brougham, which was much more like the original clarence and had room for an extra seat. The brougham became the favourite carriage of doctors and other professional men who were too staid to use a gig, tilbury or stanhope.

A feature of most eighteenth-century vehicles which immediately strikes the twentieth-century eye was the unnecessary height above the ground at which the bodies were placed. Obviously they had to be high enough above the perch for there to be no risk of the coach bottom striking the carriage when the springs played to their full extent, and the doors had to swing clear of the high back wheels, but even allowing for these factors a quite unnecessary amount of clearance—two feet was by no means uncommon—was often given and it is apparent that the vagaries of fashion prevailed over the mechanical considerations.

Part of the total height, of course, arose because large wheels gave easier riding to the passengers and easier work to the horses than small ones. For a full-scale private coach or chariot in 1790, according to Felton[1] the hind wheels were sometimes as much as 5 feet 8 inches in diameter (though 5 feet 6 inches or 5 feet 4 inches were more common), whilst the fore wheels were anything from 3 feet 2 inches to 4 feet 6 inches according to whether the perch was straight, curved or 'crane necked': that is, fitted with a wrought-iron front section shaped like an inverted U so that large front wheels could 'lock under' further than a conventional perch permitted. The wheelbase of a coach at this period was generally 9 feet 8 inches, and a chariot was usually six inches less, but in either vehicle the floor of the body was some four feet or more above the ground. Access was by means of ingenious folding steps of three, four or sometimes five inconveniently small treads, and it can be seen that it was no easy matter for a stout woman in hooped skirts, or an elderly gentleman with the gout, to climb in and out of a carriage. By 1850 wheel diameter, wheelbase and suspension clearances had been reduced so that a 'dress carriage', a landau, or other conventional vehicle needed only a two-tread step and the new perchless carriages could be entered from a single step.

The extreme height of absurdity, or absurdity of height, was reached by the 'perch-high' or 'highflyer' phaeton, beloved of the Prince of Wales (King George IV) as a young man, which carried its single seat directly over the front axle with the floorboards some 5 feet 6 inches above the ground. The hind wheels were 5 feet 8 inches or more in diameter, the front ones 4 feet 6 inches and the body was supported on an intricate combination of whip and double-elbow springs. The 'highflyer' was regarded as a neck-breaking fantasy in its own day and the thrill and danger of driving one was greatly increased when expert 'whips', such as the Prince, drove 'random'; that is, with three horses in line ahead.

Another variation on the ordinary perch carriage was the invention of Philip de Chiesa, a Piedmontese in the service of Frederick William, Duke of Prussia, who designed a carriage with two perches instead of one in 1660. These perches passed outside the extreme width of the coach body, which rested on long leather braces, one to each side, which passed right under the rockers, to which they were attached, and were anchored to blocks and adjustment windlasses on the fore and hind axle beds. This type of carriage was called the Berlin and was built in both coach and coupé form; the relatively slender resilient perches combined with the braces to give very easy suspension. With springs in place of (or supplementing) the braces the Berlin type of carriage remained popular throughout the eighteenth century, and the double perch construction allowed the body to be hung lower than usual, but by about 1820 the Berlin was absolescent. The name was revived for a type of motor body.

Nothing could be easier than to describe the brakes of eighteenth-century vehicles, for, generally speaking, they had none. The files of the patent office bristle with specifications for different forms of 'wheel retarder', but for all practical purposes the only retarder to be used was the drag shoe or skid, and the reason for this lay in the implacable opposition of professional coachman to the adoption of a more convenient form of brake. Before condemning the race of coachmen for obscurantism it must be remembered that the art of driving 'four in hand' was still relatively new during the last quarter of the eighteenth century and all professional drivers, whether they commanded four beasts or two, or but a single horse, were proud of their skill, and thought of the 'patent brake' as a contrivance only fit to help amateurs out of trouble.[2]

The drag shoe was an affair shaped rather like a deep, narrow, handle-less coal shovel which was attached to the perch by a stout chain: it normally hung from a hook adjacent to the chain anchorage, but before starting down a steep hill the coachman or postillion reined-in his horses, the footman or guard got down and placed the drag shoe under the near-hind wheel in such a way as to prevent it from turning; the vehicle then moved on with the locked wheel ploughing a furrow in the road until level ground was reached again, when the vehicle stopped and the wheel was backed out of the drag, which was then replaced on its hook.

Apart from damaging the road, the drag shoe had many other disadvantages. It was normally reserved for steep hills and at all other times every halt entailed throwing the impetus of the vehicle upon the horses; if a horse fell it was beyond the coachman's power to prevent the carriage from adding to the injury already suffered; on inclines too gentle to warrant the use of the skid the horses had all the labour of 'holding back' which was almost as fatiguing to them as the work of drawing their load up an equal slope and countless accidents were caused, particularly to the public coaches, because imprudent drivers trying to make up lost time would delay too long the necessary halt to put on the drag. Once a heavy coach got out of hand on a hill disaster was almost inevitable.

The drag shoe was, indeed, a barbarous device and yet it was still in use on coal carts, clay tumbrels and agricultural wagons until they disappeared from regular use in the third decade of this century. Brakes, as we know them, began to be fitted to private carriages occasionally in the 1830s, and although there were countless different varieties nearly all of them exerted their retarding influence by means of blocks pressing directly upon the tyres of the hind wheels; the patented part of the business concerned the means whereby the pressure was exerted and the materials used for facing the blocks. Some form of screw action was usual and the task of applying the brake was generally entrusted to the footman or guard rather than to the driver. A pedal-operated brake under the driver's control was adopted by the London General Omnibus Company in the 1860s[3] and the greater safety of the public and the saving to the horses were so obvious that some form of driver-controlled brake became common, though not universal, before the end of the century. Coachmen of the old school continued to look upon brakes as symptomatic of general decay in the proper order of things.

The business of designing a two-wheeled carriage was obviously simpler than a four-wheeler, but a nice touch was required to achieve elegant lines combined with the good balance which was essential to the well-being of the horse. Some nineteenth-century two-wheelers were fitted with sliding seats (or, occasionally, sliding bodies) so that the balance could be adjusted according to load or gradient; but in general the point of balance was fixed and the weight on the horses' collar could only be eased by the occupants leaning forward or back on steep gradients. This led to the belief that even in four-wheeled carriages it 'helped the poor horse' if the passengers leaned forwards going up hill.

The shafts constituted the main frame members of most two-wheeled vehicles, and before axle springs came into use some degree of resilient suspension was achieved by using flexible shafts made of lancewood. The owners of two-wheeled vehicles suffered relatively more than the 'carriage gentry' from the absurd legislation which, at one time, imposed a higher rate of annual tax on sprung than on unsprung carriages. Like most sumptuary laws, this was inspired by envy and kept alive by inertia: those rich enough to afford a four-wheeled carriage with the necessary horses and servants suffered relatively little from the extra impost which only represented a small proportion of their expenses, but the less well-to-do could only avoid the vexatious tax by denying themselves the luxury of riding on springs. Apart from this limitation the application of steel springs followed the same general pattern as with four-wheeled vehicles.

Also following the pattern of four-wheelers, many two-wheeled carriages, having been evolved for one individual customer, for use in some special locality or for some particular purpose then became popular and remained in production long after the original function had been forgotten. Typical of these was the dog-cart, which was sometimes made in four-wheeled form, when it differed little from a variety of phaeton. The two-wheeled dog-cart grew up out of the gig when a large locker was built in the centre of the vehicle, with back-to-back seats arranged over it, for carrying sporting dogs for shooting, coursing or those rather disgusting rat-catching contests which delighted our ancestors. The dog-locker was ventilated by louvred shutters let into the side panels, but it was soon found convenient for other purposes, and the dog-cart became the favourite vehicle of the commercial traveller, farmer, and country doctor, and a faint aura of raffishness survived from its original sporty character. Many variations on the theme were introduced and the Whitechapel cart, the Oxford, the Malvern, the Prince, the Manchester and the Beaufort[4] were but a few of the dog-cart derivatives. The louvred ventilators gave way first to dummy shutters and finally to *trompe l'œil* painting. Nowhere did tradition die harder than in the carriage trade, and some early motor cars were fitted with *dos-à-dos* bodywork in dog-cart fashion and even they were sometimes adorned with simulated louvres on the body panels.

The modern custom of hiring vehicles on annual contract to commercial firms for their representatives to use is not so modern. In his *History of Coaches* G. A. Thrupp[5] states that in 1830 one London coachworks alone supplied more than 200 vehicles a year in this way: most of these were gigs, dog-carts and tilburys. The railways put a stop to a lot of this trade, but the numbers of carriages in use steadily increased. The Treasury returns show that in 1834 duty was paid on 49,000 four-wheeled carriages and 50,000 two-wheelers (this figure included the 'taxed carts', i.e. spring-mounted four-wheelers of less than twelve pounds purchase price). In 1874 tax was paid on 150,000 four-wheelers, which included 25,000 formerly taxed separately as stage or mail vehicles, whilst the number of two-wheelers had increased to 285,000. This last figure is a little misleading, as by 1874 basket-bodied and other very light four-wheelers of less than four hundredweight paid the same tax as two-wheelers and were classified with them but the total increase, from fewer than 100,000 to within sight of the half-million, in forty years, despite the railroads, indicates that road transport was by no means moribund.

Apart from the wheel failures already dealt with in Chapter 5, many carriage breakdowns in the eighteenth century were attributable to breakage of some piece of ironwork. Poles or shafts might break occasionally, leather braces rather more frequently and some part of the timber framing from time to time, but the relative frequency of delays or accidents from broken shackle irons, springs, axle arms, perch bolts or other iron parts indicates that though the art of woodworking may have been mastered (poor workmanship or neglect being the principal causes of timber failure), metallurgy was still in its infancy. The advances in foundry work and forging, together with the advance of metallurgical science early in the nineteenth century, resulted in improved reliability and in the substitution of metal for wood in axles, perches, and so forth. According to some contemporary Jeremiahs this was accompanied by a corresponding decline in the quality and workmanship of the timber parts. This seems to be too pessimistic a view and by present-day standards the care the nineteenth-century coach- or cart-builder took in selecting, seasoning and working his timber puts modern wood-working to shame.

Though the workmanship put into horsed vehicles was generally good, it must be said that their design was often lacking in science. It was a trade in which empirical methods went hand in hand with tradition, and certain fallacies were lovingly cherished by so-called practical men long after they had been exploded by theorists. Conversely some theorists managed to establish practices based on faulty reasoning.

The unnecessary height above ground of most eighteenth-century carriages has already been remarked upon, and in part this sprang from a belief, firmly held by coachmen and coachbuilders, that the shorter the wheelbase the more easily the carriage 'followed after the horses' and the less, in consequence, the draught. This seems to have been the result of false reasoning from observing the un-handiness of some overlong and ill-contrived vehicles such as the broad-wheel stage-wagons, and the magnificent but almost useless State Coach of 1761, which was often quoted as an example of how *not* to build a carriage.

Another factor in favour of a short wheelbase was the English coachmen's preference (in contrast to Continental practice) for having the horses as close as possible to the carriage, and the coach-man's seat as far as possible over the horses' backs. This led to placing the forecarriage as far back as the steering requirements allowed. In private carriages the unreasonable reduction of the wheelbase was neither so prevalent nor so dangerous as it was in the public coaches, the design of which was very much influenced by those beliefs. A great many nineteenth-century writers, such as W. Bridges Adams[6] and Joseph Storrs Fry,[7] remarked on the folly of having a 4 foot 6 inch or 5 foot wheelbase for a coach carrying, perhaps, twelve or more people and half a ton of luggage several feet above the centre of gravity.

Joseph Fry wrote in 1820, amongst other things, that: 'The whole of our coach system is unphilosophical and barbarous', and went on to deal with the advantages of a change in thinking:

. . . it may be objected that the consequence of lengthening the carriage and lowering the load will be that the weight would follow more heavily after the horses. It would certainly be difficult to answer such objectors who would be likely to be of the class called *men of experience*, that is to say, men brought up in a routine of practice yet totally ignorant of principles. It seems as though they have a notion that the fore-wheel of a carriage, when *closely followed* by the hind-wheel, makes haste out of its way; as a little boy at school, when persued by a bigger boy, runs as fast as he can . . . All these notions about the necessity of horses being *close to their work*, and of wheels following as nearly as possible after each other, and of coaches that are loaded high running lighter than when the load is low, are completely refuted by the actual experiments of Richard Lovel Edgeworth . . .[8]

The practice of having the fore wheels smaller than the hind ones was also indefensible in one respect. It was clear that large wheels lightened the horses' labour by comparison with small ones by riding more easily over rough ground, although one author, Joseph Jacob,[9] put forward a learned but not wholly convincing argument that though large wheels were advantageous on level ground they increased the draught on inclines in proportion to their diameter. As, however, he admitted that this proposition held good only on perfectly smooth surfaces, it was generally disregarded and both practical and scientific men agreed that the larger the wheel the better, within the limits of convenience.

It was also generally agreed that the traces ideally should run in a horizontal, or nearly horizontal, line from the hames to the centres of the fore wheels: this was not possible with the conventional layout of a four-wheeled carriage, and the usual compromise was to strike a line from the horses' shoulders to a point just below the naves of the hind wheels.

As any man who had pushed a wheelbarrow knew, too small a wheel often made a barrow unusable on bad ground unless it was pulled rather than pushed, and if the wheels of a carriage had to be of unequal sizes it was obvious that it was better to have the smaller wheels behind rather than in front. All these theoretical considerations came into collision with the practical need, with a centre-pivoted steering axle, to reduce the diameter of the fore wheels in order to reduce the size of the turning circle by allowing the front wheels to pass under the coachman's box. This led to the further disadvantage that the greater the angle to which the fore axle could 'lock over' the less the stability of the carriage and the greater the tendency to overturn.

There were two notable nineteenth-century inventions to over-come the difficulties: one sprang from the fertile mind of W. Bridges Adams, one of the first men to try to combine traditional carriage-building techniques with engineering principles, who designed vehicles which were, in effect, hinged behind the forecarriage so that the front axle did not have to pivot on a perch bolt and the front wheels could be as large as the back ones without limiting the lock. Adams published designs for different forms of 'equirotal' carriages, as he called them, and a few equirotal omnibuses were put on the London streets in the early 1840s; but despite the encouragement of the Duke of Wellington, ever ready to try a new idea, the equirotal principle did not prevail.

Of much greater importance and even less initial success was the ancestor of the method of steering now universal, which is known as Ackermann steering. This system had been proposed as far back as 1714, but a German coachbuilder, Georg Lenkensperger, worked out the correct geometrical forms of the parts and produced a carriage embodying the principle in 1816. The English patent was held on his behalf by his friend Rudolf Ackermann, the famous print seller. By arranging each front wheel on a separately pivoting 'stub' axle, and linking the two together by an arrangement of arms and levers so angled and proportioned that the inside wheel turned through a greater angle than the outside wheel in proportion to the radius of the curve to be described, a much greater degree of stability was achieved than with the centre-pivoted axle, and the size of the wheels could be increased without unduly limiting the turning circle.

In his account of his attempts to interest the carriage trade in this invention Ackermann recorded the following dialogue with an unnamed London coachbuilder.

Ackermann   Pray, Sir, what think you of this invention?
Coachbuilder   Sir, it will not do.
Ackermann   And why, Sir, will it not do?
Coachbuilder   Because, Sir, it will not do.

Before condemning coachbuilders as a race of obscurantists it must be remembered that whether he knew it or not Mr Acker-mann's sparring partner in this exchange had one compelling reason for saying the new invention 'would not do'. Fashion and tradition

10 Scale model of a Surrey waggon of c. 1820

11 Sir George Armitage's phaeton, c. 1770

12 Except for the undersprings and some other details this dress chariot of
c. 1890 might well have been made in 1790

13 The Hungarian Britzka was much improved by English coachbuilders:
a London-made example of c. 1818

have always played a larger part than engineering requirements in the design of vehicles both horsed and horseless, and in 1820, when Ackermann suffered this rebuff, several centuries of tradition dictated the use of unequal-sized wheels and centre-pivoted axles. That the former represented an unscientific compromise dictated by the latter did not matter to the ordinary vehicle buyer or user. Seen through the spectacles of 1820, carriages with equal-sized wheels would have seemed wrong and would inevitably have been condemned as ugly. The tradition that vehicles *must* have smaller wheels in front than behind, as though by divine ordination, survived the introduction of the motor car; although all but a tiny minority of the horseless carriages which began to be sold to the public in 1888 had Ackermann steering it was not until 1900 that equal-sized wheels began to be acceptable.

Despite all the ingenuity which went into spring suspension, and the excellent results the best carriage-builders achieved, certain improper practices were perpetuated in spring-making for no better reason than that things always had been done in a certain way. The ordinary blacksmith was fully capable of making a new plate, or leaf, to replace a broken one and was often called upon to make complete springs, but spring-smithing soon developed as a specialist trade, highly skilled but hampered by certain traditional practices, some of which were founded on little better than superstition.

This particularly applied to the process of 'middling' the individual spring leaves by hammering them before the hardening and tempering processes in such a way as to lower their centres below their edges. The two outer leaves were 'middled' only on their inner faces, but all the others were 'middled' on both sides. The custom may have originated in an attempt to toughen or work-harden the surface, but it was of doubtful value and had the obvious demerit of reducing the areas of contact, increasing the risk of fatigue and fracture by concentrating all the work on the edges and providing a perfect trap for water. In 1837 Bridges Adams summed up on behalf of the scientific observer (he was not the first) in these terms:

It is evident that the whole process of spring-making is defective. In the first place, the plates should be tapered from the hoop to the points; which they are not, but merely at the points. In the next place the plates should bear flat on each other thoughout their width; which they do not, and being thinner in the middle than at the edges they are more likely to break. In the next place, not being tempered in a large fire with a measured and accurate degree of heat, but depending entirely on the eye and skill of the workman, it is evident they must be liable to inaccuracy . . . The 'middling' process produces a large hollow space between every two plates. Into these recesses the rain or the washing water finds its way and forms a magazine of rust, eating away the hardened surface in which most of the elasticity of the plates resides . . .[10]

Mr Adams's views on spring-smithing were shared by many other scientifically inclined observers, at least one of whom, some fifty years later, paid him the doubtful compliment of plagiarizing his exact words in a treatise on coachbuilding—without acknowledgement, of course. The spring specialists, however, persisted with their unscientific methods (although the larger firms introduced better heat-treatment methods) until the present century was well advanced and the motor-car industry was obliged to adopt various expedients. The Austin Co., for example, at one time interleaved their springs with zinc in order to increase the bearing surfaces, and Rolls-Royce ground and polished the spring leaves made to their specification by outside suppliers. The logical step was taken in the 1920s by the Lanchester Co. when, being exasperated by the professionals' work, they set up their own spring-making plant and produced their famous cantilever springs with some eighty-five to ninety per cent of the surfaces of the contiguous leaves in contact by comparison with the fifteen to twenty per cent of the specialists'.

Ash was the timber almost invariably used for body framing and before the end of the nineteenth century complaints were heard that coachbuilders were finding it difficult to get English ash in large enough pieces. American ash was extensively used, but it was much more prone to rot than the denser English variety. Honduras mahogany was the best material for panelling, as it was straight grained and dense, took paint well, could be had up to four feet in width and could be curved in the steam box to quite acute curves without splitting. For flat panels in lower-grade work American birch was extremely suitable and an American variety of cedar was used as a foundation for roof and quarter panels which were intended to be covered with glazed leather. One of the early nineteenth-century innovations was the adoption of invisible joints for roof and quarter panels which allowed them to be made watertight without any covering. This gave a lighter and more elegant effect and allowed for 'razor edge' sharpness of angles; Baltic deals or pine were used for these roofs (and for floors), but because the older leather-covered roofs and top quarters had necessarily been kept from cracking by applications of oil and blacking, tradition demanded that the new-style upper quarters were also finished in black, although, quite often, some other colour might have been more suitable. The tradition of black quarters and roof is still not quite extinct.

In carriage design the British tended to be short on invention, but their talent for improvement was soon manifest. Most of the carriage styles were of Continental origin, but were so improved by the English coachbuilders as to be virtually unrecognizable after a short while; and other factors than the snobbery which prompts some of the upper class of all races to assert their superiority by buying foreign luxuries promoted a brisk demand for English carriages thoughout Western Europe. By 1820 it had become accepted that English carriages were usually superior in design and always better in appearance and finish than their Continental counterparts. The upholstery, trimming and equipment of the interiors were of superb quality, even on relatively inexpensive vehicles, whilst the art of the coachpainter was developed in England to a very high degree.

Most English coachbuilding concerns, until late in the nineteenth century, ground their own pigments and mixed their own paints and varnishes from the finest procurable materials in order to be certain of the excellent results which made English coachwork famous. From the preliminary priming to the final varnishing some forty to fifty coats of paint of different kinds were used, each coat being meticulously rubbed down with sand-paper, powdered pumice and whiting before putting on the next. The mere preliminary priming and flatting often called for twelve or fifteen operations before the first ground colours were laid on, and the inner surfaces of the body panels, before trimming, were made waterproof by gluing thin canvas over them as a 'key' to hold two or three coats of Brunswick black and white lead.

The blemish-free surface and deep lustre achieved by the best coachpainters has never been surpassed, and even relatively humble vehicles were finished to a standard considerably better than that of the most expensive modern motor car. Cheap labour made this possible, but by the standards of the time carriage painters were well paid: in 1857 a foreman painter could command three to four guineas a week and his underlings received between one and three pounds according to their experience and skill.[11]

The labour put into coachpainting was not only done to secure a beautiful finish but to make the woodwork durable in the worst that the English climate could do. When one considers the different varieties of wood, each with its own characteristic reaction to changes of temperature or humidity, joined together in a great variety of ways, and the scarcity of plane surfaces (nearly all carriage panelling and framing being curved in more than one plane), the importance of making all the parts totally impervious to damp will be appreciated.

Unfortunately the materials available were less stable than some of the modern synthetic paints and varnishes, and the ammoniacal vapours given off by the dung-heaps found near most coach-houses, particularly in town, combined with the sulphuric acid gas from coal fires and abrasive road dust to craze and dull the varnished surfaces fairly quickly. To preserve the original gloss it was necessary to have the work rubbed-down and revarnished fairly often—once a year was recommended—but even when this was neglected (as it invariably was on all but the conveyances of the 'carriage gentry') though the gloss might grow dull the paint itself would stand for half a century or more without peeling or letting water in to the many joints it protected.

Vehicle design may often have been imperfect from the engineers' point of view, but aesthetically it ranged from good to superb. The subject of the carriage as a work of art is too large to discuss here, but there is no doubt that it is right to consider the carriage, horsed or horseless, as a work of art as well as a piece of machinery; and many of the eighteenth- and nineteenth-century coachbuilders were artists.

We recieve a slightly imperfect picture of carriage work from most contemporary illustrations, before photography, as the line engravings in books and catalogues suffered from a convention which decreed that the wheels of passenger carriages must always be made to appear more delicate than they were. Not only did the artists 'thin down' the spokes and felloes to an impossible degree, but very often wheels were depicted with fewer spokes than they must have had in actuality. If allowance be made for this conventional distortion it may still be seen what mastery of line, proportion and curve was achieved. This mastery extended to relatively humble vehicles, and in its way, a hay-wain is as handsome as a barouche. Naturally, there were some ugly vehicles, but most were good-looking and many were positively beautiful.

One very curious feature of carriage design, aesthetically speaking, is that it went in the opposite direction to furniture, architecture and interior decorating. The gentleman's carriage of, say, 1770 would be relatively overdecorated and less satisfactorily proportioned than his house and its contents, which by contrast were impeccably restrained and harmonious; but a hundred years later when furniture design had sunk to the depths of tasteless elaboration and gaudy decoration combined with total want of proportion, the carriage-builders were producing designs of masterly proportions, in which beautifully restrained curves were offset by harmonious colour schemes and just sufficient decoration to enhance the purity of line.

The contrast between the riotous extravagance of the State Coach designed by Sir William Chambers for King George III in 1761, and the subtle beauty of the State Landau built for Queen Victoria's visit to Ireland in 1900 says all that needs to be said on this score.

CHAPTER SEVEN

Stage and Mail

There is a striking parallel between the great days of coaching in Britain and of steamboating on the Mississippi. In each case the heyday was very short, less than fifty years, and each mode of transport captured the public imagination. Mark Twain's description of the deference paid to the steamboat pilot, and the competition for the post of honour on the bench in the wheelhouse, corresponds to the rivalry for a seat on the coachman's box; his account of the bustling quayside of St Louis at steamboat time marches with the many vivid descriptions of coach departure time at the Belle Sauvage or Magpie and Stump; and the races between *Red Rover* and *Quicksilver*, or between stage and mail, were as fiercely fought and exciting as the famous contest between those swift, snorting monsters the *Natchez* and the *Robert E. Lee*.

Stage-coaches of a kind certainly existed in the seventeenth century, but as the name was very loosely used it may well be that many of the vehicles described as coaches differed little from the covered stage-wagons which carried passengers as well as goods. By the middle of the eighteenth century the public coach almost invariably resembled the ordinary private coach except for the addition, usually, of a vast basket carried on iron stays between the hind wheels. This was known as the 'conveniency', and if space permitted half-fare passengers were permitted to ride in it, accommodating themselves as best they might amongst the baggage and parcels. Until the nineteenth century it was common practice for the coachman to insist that the half-fare passengers should save his horses by walking up hills; if the going were very bad the 'insides' might well have to walk also, so that even the payment of something between 6*d*. and 1*s*. a mile did not guarantee that one rode all the way.

Except for a little backwards-facing perch for the guard, there were

108

no roof seats on the early stage-coaches, though one or two passengers could be accommodated on the box. Most coachmen, however, allowed 'illegal' passengers to cling to the roof as best they might and the money they paid for this privilege was split between driver and guard. Finding it impossible to stop this practice, the proprietors made a virtue of necessity by fixing a rudimentary seat across the leading edge of the coach-roof where three or four customers could perch uncomfortably, bracing their feet against the back of the fore boot. This was not, at that time, part of the coach body, but a 'Salisbury boot' formed of leather-covered ironwork rigidly mounted above the front axle beds. The boot and box seat, therefore, were unsprung and the swaying of the coach body on its whip springs and braces kept the knees of the outside passengers in perpetual bellows-like motion. The notion that the boot and the driver's seat might be attached to the coach body, so as to give the driver the benefit of the springs, was sternly resisted by most proprietors on the grounds that the men would become dozy and idle if they were not constantly hammered and pounded over the rough roads. The notion that a man might work better for a little comfort was tantamount to heresy, but by the end of the eighteenth century common sense prevailed; fore boot and box seat were 'framed into' the coach body proper and a similar hind boot, in place of the wickerwork 'conveniency', supported a full-width forwards-facing seat for guard and passengers and also provided a footrest for more passengers carried on a back-wards-facing seat across the rear edge of the coach-roof. The 'traditional' stage-coach of Christmas card and calendar had arrived.

These changes were accompanied by improvements to the sus-pension; the whip and elbow springs and braces of the mid-eighteenth century took up a lot of space and despite the complexity of interlaced check straps allowed too much pitching and side-sway. As the profitability of allowing more and more passengers and freight on the roof became apparent many different types of suspen-sion were tried, and a number of 'patent safety' coaches took the road—generally for short periods only. Early in the nineteenth century the arrangement of 'telegraph' springs, described in Chapter 4, was used on most of the public coaches; as well as being more reliable than the earlier forms of springing, and more stable, the 'telegraph' springs allowed the centre of gravity to be lowered. Although the belief prevailed that a high-pitched vehicle 'followed the horses' better than a low one, the folly of concentrating too much weight too far above ground became apparent. Indeed, the legislature, urged by a Mr Gammon and alarmed by the frequency of coach accidents, took a hand and an Act was passed in 1788 (28 Geo. III, c. 57) limiting the roof load to six people, of whom only two were supposed to share the driver's box. This Act did not go so far as Mr Gammon had proposed and although the penalties it specified were severe it was widely evaded. The coachman was liable to a fine of two pounds (or four pounds if he was also the proprietor) for each unlawful passenger and evasion was supposedly prevented by making a common informer eligible for half the amount of the fine: even at this price few took the risk of informing.

Two years later the Government recognized that the Act had failed and another was passed which limited the outside passengers to one on the box and four on the roof for a coach drawn by three or more horses.With fewer than three horses the limits were one on the box and three on the roof, with the proviso that two-horse coaches might take four passengers on the roof within a twenty-five miles radius of the General Post Office. This Act made the turnpike-keepers custodians of the law by enacting that they should collect a five-shilling fine for every illegal passenger before passing the coach through the gate. Although the penalty for evasion was imprisonment without the option of a fine, most 'pike-keepers' took advantage of the coachmen's interest in carrying extra fares, and for a consideration connived at the illegal passengers dismounting just before the gate, walking through and remounting on the other side.

In the new century control of these and other matters grew more efficient; coach proprietors had to keep to the law or risk withdrawal of their licences, and the day was passed when a bribe or a threat would suffice. New Acts were passed which discouraged the building of very lofty coaches: the permitted number of outside passengers for a four-horse coach in 1806 was twelve in summer and ten in winter, but although the new-style coaches were less unstable than the older variety this was still a dangerous load, and a new Act in 1811 specified that *no* passengers or luggage should be placed on the roof of a coach which, in conjunction with the normal track width of 4 feet 6 inches, stood more than 8 feet 9 inches high unladen; up to twelve passengers, and goods, might be carried at a greater level than two feet above the roof-top provided the highest point of the inanimate burden was not more than 10 feet 9 inches above the ground. This was followed by another Act in 1832 which permitted the full complement of passengers only if the top of the inanimate load was no more than 8 feet 9 inches above ground. In view of the very short wheelbase and the inherently unstable centre-pivoted steering-axle a fully loaded coach, even under this regulation, was still almost certain to overturn in event of an accident and accidents were distressingly common and often involved fatalities.

The number of inside passengers was supposedly limited to four for the ordinary public day coaches. Some special designs capable of seating six (or sometimes more), were evolved, but did not come into general use, and many of the larger, slower night coaches were also licensed for six 'insides'. It may be assumed that these inspired some coach operators to pretend that their four-passenger coaches could actually accommodate six 'insides'; hence the irascible Mr Dowler's threat to the stage-coach guard that if he attempted to fit '. . . six people into an infernal box made for four' he would 'take a post-chaise and bring an action'.[1]

Because the golden age of coaching captured the public imagination and is now seen through a romantic mist it is too readily overlooked that it was a short-lived age. The really regular and swift stage-coach services to which the industry of the country owed so much only came to maturity as a result of competition with the mail-coaches—and the first mail-coach service dates only from 1784. It is also not generally realized that the art of driving more than two horses 'in hand', in which lay the essence of coaching, was also a very late invention.

Nor is it known who first practised the art and, almost certainly, it was not the discovery of an individual but the result of spontaneous innovations and experiments made by different people at different times. It is fairly certain that a stage-coach (or a private one for that matter) which went with four horses during most of the first half of the eighteenth century had the leaders managed by a postillion and only when it went with two (as most of the early coaches did on easy stretches) was it really 'in hand'. Early woodcuts illustrating coach advertisements and waybills, though rather obscure, seem to show that when leaders were used they drew from the same tugs as the wheelers. That is, the traces from the lead horses' collars passed outside the wheel horses' traces and were made fast to the main splinter bar; horses harnessed in this way were occasionally driven tandem from the box, but it was a hazardous enough method of controlling two horses and would have been virtually impossible with four. The addition of leading bars, known as 'swingletrees', attached to the pole by swivel hooks, seems to have been a mid-century innovation and only then did four-in-hand driving become regularly practised; surprisingly little was written on the subject until 'Nimrod'[2] wrote his famous articles for the *Sporting Magazine* at the turn of the century. This is understandable enough when one reflects that the professional coach operator was too busy, and the professional driver too illiterate, to write about a subject which doubtless formed the topic of conversation wherever coaching men met.

It is not easy therefore (nor for our purpose is it necessary) to be precise about the changes in harnessing and bitting, and the introduction of such innovations as coupling reins and bearing reins which took place during the fifty years when four-in-hand driving became an established and enviable art. Art it undeniably was (for there was little of science about it)—one which called for strength as well as skill and one which began to attract amateurs, or 'gentlemen coachmen' as 'Nimrod' called them, who took pleasure in 'tooling' a public coach (often to the dismay of the other passengers), having lavishly tipped the official driver into allowing this supposedly forbidden practice. A number of four-in-hand clubs sprang up in the new century, of which the oldest, the Benson Driving Club, was founded in 1807. Their members met to hold driving contests, using their 'mail phaetons' or 'brakes',* to eat and drink and to discuss such esoteric mysteries as the best method of 'catching the whip'; whether the little finger should press down upon or pass under the rein; how the draught and coupling reins should best be arranged between which fingers; and whether the left hand should be held high, bringing the reins close to the chest, or low down beside the left knee or extended, with straight elbow, above the lap. These last points, which were fundamentally matters of personal taste or convenience, became matters of propriety or fashion and were

* Mail phaeton: a light sporting carriage with elevated box seat for two and dickey for a groom, the perch, springs, axles, wheels, etc., all of regulation 'mail pattern' scaled down. Brake, originally (and correctly) 'break': a skeleton vehicle for breaking horses to carriage work, also used for exercising and then developed into shooting-brake, luggage-brake, etc.

argued as hotly and fruitlessly as the present controversy about driving horseless carriages with arms extended or akimbo.

In the eighteenth century the mail service was concerned only with letters and was divided into four sections. Through mails, or London letters, were those directed to the capital along the through routes. Country letters were those which went to London via one of the through routes and then were forwarded to their destination, as, for example, a letter from Bristol to Shrewsbury. Bye-letters were taken up and set down at intermediate points on a through route, and the bye-post also served the immediate neighbourhood of such points. The cross-post linked major provincial towns such as Exeter and Bristol. The postmasters were royal monopolists until 1780, and therefore had the advantage of being the only people entitled to provide the relay service of horses not only for carrying the mails but for the traveller. In 1780 the business of 'posting' was thrown open to public contract as far as the 'travelling posts' were concerned, though the carriage of letters remained a royal monopoly as it is today. As the fees for letter-carrying were paid on delivery, there were ample opportunities for postmasters to 'understand' one another about the bye- and cross-posts which never came under the eyes of the G.P.O. officials in London; consequently these mails were often 'farmed' for a set annual sum.

John Palmer of Bath was the man primarily responsible for the mail coach and it is probable that his interest in the postal service was aroused by the example of Ralph Allen, also of Bath, who had greatly improved the cross- and bye-postal services, which he 'farmed', and had made himself a comfortable fortune in the process. Palmer's aim was to improve security as well as to hasten the post and their Lordships the Postmaster-General* might well have rested content with the slowness, the frequent robbery and the not infrequent murder of the mounted post-boys had a new stage-coach service not been put to work on the Bristol–Bath–London route in 1782. The new coaches made the journey in seventeen hours against the thirty-eight taken by the riding-post, and carried parcels for delivery

* This curious designation is correct according to the usage of the time, as the *office* of Postmaster-General was invariably then vested in two noblemen, members of the Cabinet. According to etiquette it was proper to recognize the singularity of the office but the duality of its holders by the form 'Their Lordships the Post Master General'.

at the terminal and intermediate stages. It was against the law for letters to be carried by any but a private servant or the Royal Mail, but no law could stop people making their letters into parcels and sending them by stage-coach. The loss of revenue to the Post Office was not confined to that incurred on the Bristol–Bath–London service, but, being easily verified, it was used to add force to John Palmer's argument that if the mails were carried under armed guard in special passenger coaches the robberies would cease, the posts could be hastened and the costs reduced. At that time the Post Office paid threepence a mile to the postmasters who horsed the through-posts and delivered and collected the cross- and bye-posts in their districts. Palmer proposed that the same rate be paid initially to contractors who should furnish coaches and horses to execute his plan, but it was clearly in his mind that if the coachmasters were allowed to keep the profits from passenger traffic carried on the coaches it would be possible progressively to reduce the mileage contract rates as the business grew.

There was a great deal of opposition both inside and outside the Post Office, and two years of political intrigue followed Palmer's submission of his proposals. The advocates of the one-horse mail-cart, which was already in use in some parts of the country, were hotly opposed to the mail-coach idea. A fast-trotting horse in the shafts of a light cart could certainly carry the mails faster than a mounted man carrying a similar load, and the sponsors of the mail-cart also claimed greater security; but they had a sharp set-back when the first of a new type of cart, with a supposedly thief-proof iron locker, was way-laid by highwaymen and its contents stolen. A three-volume report on Palmer's proposals consisted almost wholly of objections. One of them, raised by the district surveyors who supervised the horsed-mail in the four major divisions of the country, was to the effect that if any lives were lost through the armed guard putting up a fight if a coach was attacked the Post Office might be involved in a murder charge. This rather fanciful piece of reasoning matched the official conclusion that: 'the present arrangements of the post cannot possibly be improved. . . . ' The words have a sadly familiar ring. To refute the objections and to support his argument further John Palmer made a survey of all the important stage-coach services throughout the country with details of their time-tables, charges, and horsing arrangements.

A fortunate shift in the political wind came to Palmer's aid. George III contrived to get rid of the Shelbourne administration, which he detested, and appointed the young Pitt as Prime Minister; a general election in March 1784 supported the monarch's apparently high-handed action by returning Pitt with a very large majority, and Pitt had been convinced of the merits of Palmer's plan for more than a year. He used his authority to overrule the Post Office and authorized Palmer to organize an experimental service on the Bristol–Bath–London route at his own expense.

Although time was short, Palmer was able to make contracts with five inn- and horse-keepers to horse the service at the current rate of threepence a mile, although far more horses were needed than for the ordinary post. These agreements were only signed on Saturday, 31 July, and the service was due to start on the following Monday. In addition to providing an armed guard Palmer had undertaken to better the seventeen-hour stage-coach schedule by one hour, and few people believed he could do it. The first mail-coach left Bristol at four in the afternoon of 2 August; it was an ordinary stage-coach with the roof seating removed and a stout padlocked mail chest mounted above the hind axle bed; the armed guard sat beside the driver; no outside passengers were allowed, but all four inside places were filled; the coach arrived at the General Post Office in London promptly at eight o'clock the next morning. This was, as promised, an hour less than the best stage-coach time. The London mail left the G.P.O. at eight o'clock in the evening, reached Bath at ten the following day and arrived at the Bristol terminal at noon.

The mail-coach service had started, a new era had arrived, and before the trial period was over it was clear that Palmer's optimism was justified; postal revenue on the Bristol–London route increased and the passenger places could have been sold several times over. Despite continued opposition, Palmer was ordered to extend his range and during the spring and summer of 1785 mail-coaches took over the cross-post from Bristol to Portsmouth and were put to work on important through-routes such as London to Dover, Portsmouth, Exeter, Leeds, Manchester, Birmingham, Liverpool and Shrewsbury. This was only the start, but well before the end of the century Great Britain could boast the fastest, safest and cheapest mail service in the world, and the beauty of it was that it was achieved without the taxpayer having to buy a single coach, horse, harness, stable or any other equipment beyond that needed for the guards who were enrolled as Post Office employees two years after the service started.

The Post Office laid down stringent regulations and time schedules, but the work was done by contractors who were allowed to make a very small profit from the governmental mileage allowance and a reasonable profit from the passengers. Within a short while the expression 'as regular as the mail' had passed into the language and the mail-coach men never had any shortage of custom. It was as happy a liaison between a nationalized industry and private enterprise as one is likely to find.

It is possible here only to touch briefly on the political and administrative history of the mail-coach service. In 1786 Palmer was appointed Surveyor and Comptroller-General of the Post Office at a salary of £1,500 a year plus the repayment of some of the money he had laid out and, ultimately, an agreement that he should have two and a half per cent of all Post Office revenue above £300,000 a year, which was the estimated value of the posts at the time the mail-coaches started work.[3] Although the service continued to grow quickly, there were many internal dissensions and intrigues, over some of which Palmer acted wrongly or incautiously and, in one instance, with apparent dishonesty. In 1792 he was dismissed, but not disgraced; Pitt realized that the commerce of the realm could not have been so vastly increased had the mails remained as slow and uncertain as they were before Palmer's reforms. His dismissal was disguised by reorganizing and renaming departments and he was granted a pension of £3,000 a year. In 1813 the House of Commons gave public recognition of the country's debt to Palmer, and of the injustice of his removal, by awarding him £50,000 as compensation for the loss of the two and a half per cent bonus which had been promised on his appointment and cancelled on his dismissal. Palmer lived five years to enjoy this handsome award.

His successor, under the new title of Surveyor and Comptroller of the Inland Office, was Charles Bonner, who had been his protégé and deputy and had helped to engineer his downfall; but he did not last long in the job, and Palmer's mantle really fell upon Thomas Hasker, who was promoted from Superintendent of Mail Coaches to Surveyor and Superintendent of the Mail Coaches. The insertion of the word 'the' signified that the mail-coach system was officially regarded as an essential part of the postal service. Essential it certainly was, but it might well have foundered without Hasker. Shrewd, energetic, intelligent, a strict but humane disciplinarian, unimpressed by rank without merit, humorous and blessed with the rare gift for getting the best out of people, Thomas Hasker was to the mail-coach service what Samuel Pepys had been to the Royal Navy.

Figure 3 Besant's patent coach 1786

One of the early weaknesses of the service with which Palmer's opponents made much play was the weakness of the coaches themselves. Within a short time the contractors found their ordinary stage-coaches, modified for mail service, were racked to bits by the strain of keeping to time over bad roads, and breakdowns became more and more frequent. In 1787 Palmer's attention was drawn to the specification of John Besant's 'Patent Improved Wheel Carriage' which the inventor clearly hoped would be adopted for the mail service, as the drawing which accompanied his specification showed the royal coat of arms boldly emblazoned on the door panel (a distinction reserved for the Royal Mail). Palmer thought well enough of the idea to order a trial just before leaving to investigate the French postal system, but on his return he found that his deputy (and eventual usurper) Charles Bonner had gone further and committed the Post Office to a contract for the patent coaches.

In 1791 Besant joined forces with John Vidler of Millbank, who owned one of the largest carriage-building concerns in England, and the monopoly in the supply of mail-coaches was transferred to Besant & Vidler and finally to Vidler and Co. when John Besant died in the following December. There was some jobbery about the transaction, as Charles Bonnor had become involved with Besant and appears to have been instrumental in organizing the association with Vidler; the exposure of these arrangements by Palmer led to the friction between the two men. It could be argued that the Post Office might have been better off if they had bought-out Besant & Vidler's monopoly and become coachbuilders and masters on their own account, but this was not done until 1836 when the original contract expired. The arrangements were that all the mail contractors had to use the officially approved coaches and these were rented from Vidler and Company at the rate of twopence half-penny per 'double mile'— that is, a mile either way in each coach's out-and-home journey. Vidler had to repair and maintain the coaches according to a very strict plan, and although it may be that the country might have saved money if the Post Office had owned their own vehicles from the start, it must be said that the servicing arrangements were very rigorously enforced and so admirably executed that mail-coach standards of efficiency and smartness could be matched only by the richest and most fastidious private owners of carriages.

The maintenance contract was in addition to the mileage-hire contract, but it also was based upon distance. The coaches used on the cross-post routes were cared for on a similar basis by provincial contractors. On some of these routes the mails were carried in ordinary stage-coaches, which thus became mail-coaches for, perhaps, only part of their journey. When carrying mails the official guard took charge, the Post Office schedules were observed and the number of outside passengers reduced.

One suspects that much of the merit of Besant's 'improved wheel carriage' originally rested in good workmanship and the inventor's skilful wording of his specification, for only two of the novel features of the design remained in use after a short while. One of the claims was that in the event of an overturn the suspension made the coach self-righting, so that: '. . . the overturning of the carriage will only set the body down on its bottom between the fore and hind wheels when they lay flat on the ground'. It is not possible to determine

14 Georgian exuberance: the State Coach designed by Sir William Chambers
for King George III in 1761

15 Victorian restraint: the Irish State Landau of 1900

16 The first mail coach of 1784 - adapted from an ordinary stage coach

17 Standard pattern mail coach, built at Millbank in 1827 and in service until 1842

from the drawings how this miracle was to be achieved, and an engineer as eminent as Matthew Boulton wrote that the coach was: '. . . a vehicle loaded with iron trappings and the greatest complication of unmechanical contrivances jumbled together I ever witnessed. The coach swings sideways with a sickly sway . . .'

The inventor also claimed that his 'compound perch' admitted of: '. . . the axle trees pressing against the forepart of the boxes of the wheels, whereby the body of the carriage assists the horses'. This suggests that Mr Besant might have been one of those who tried to find the perpetual motion in an overbalancing wheel or in a device for setting a spring to wind up a spring; but his patent brake (at a time when ordinary carriages had no brakes at all) was the direct ancestor of the modern 'overrun brake' for trailers. It consisted of a leather-faced band brake acting on a grooved rim attached to the inner face of the nave of the near hind wheel; this was actuated by a leather strap which passed under the curved bottom of the coach body and was made fast just below the driver's seat on the fore boot, which was, as on the ordinary coaches, rigidly mounted above the front axle tree. The theory was that as the coach started downhill the flexibility of the suspension was enough to allow the body to swing forward and, as the inventor said, this: 'strains the strap "D" and causes the gripe to impede the motion of the wheel in proportion to the descent of the hill'. As no more was heard of this ingenious idea it may be assumed that the suspension was also flexible enough to allow the brake to be jerked on spasmodically over bumpy stretches of level or uphill going.

Besant's pedal-released steering-catch also passed into limbo: this was intended to prevent the common accident of a sudden sharp turn at speed allowing the wheels to 'go on the lock'. That is, to turn far enough for the inside wheel to foul the perch or underbody and overturn the vehicle. The catch was supposed to limit the turning circle unless it was released in order to manoeuvre slowly round particularly tight turns.

The two features of Besant's design which were of undoubted value were the 'mail axle' (see Chapter 5) and the framing of a combined rear boot and guard's seat into the coach body. It is not quite clear from Besant's original specification whether the axle and wheel-securing arrangements were of the true 'mail axle' type or whether they were of the form devised at about that time by William

Saunders.[4] A later patent (No. 1574) granted to Besant in 1791 gives full details of the 'mail axle' as it was known, almost unaltered, throughout the nineteenth century.

The wheels themselves were still liable to fail, as the Post Office records show, but the improved axle and wheel-box virtually abolished the hazard of wheels coming off unexpectedly, and also allowed the bearings to run for long periods without attention; although, in practice, Post Office regulations demanded that they be examined and lubricated daily. The new arrangement of guard's seat and hind boot was much neater than the old, and the iron, or iron-bound, boot lid, in addition to a stout padlock, was made doubly secure by being directly below the guard's feet as he sat in his place. Passengers' luggage went in the fore boot and the hind one was sacred to the Post Office. It was, at first, immune from search, like a diplomatic bag, but this immunity had to be suspended as some guards were tempted to use it for carrying forbidden parcels. Letters only were carried by the Royal Mail until 1883, and parcels were the business of stage-coach or common carrier; therefore the speed of the mail-coaches made them very attractive to those furtive and irrepressible gentlemen who had occasion to send a brace of pheasants or a salmon to Town by the quickest means.

It is not quite clear whether Vidler or some other coachbuilder was responsible for making the fore boot and coachman's box seat part of the coach body. It is likely that it was one of those innovations which was adopted by different people more or less simultaneously, but some authorities[5] credit the idea to John Ward, of Squerries in Kent, who was an enthusiastic 'gentlemen coachman', known also as 'the father of fox-hunting', who had often 'tooled' the old Gloucester-Cheltenham heavy coach and was thus in a position to appreciate the unnecessary discomfort of the unsprung fore boot. The new arrangement was quite well established by 1806, though several of the older coaches remained in use for some years; and the general adoption of 'telegraph' springs took place at about the same time. The new-style coaches, mail or stage, were neater in appearance, had more baggage space and were also lower and safer. Further reduction in height to meet the needs of new legislation was made by using a curved perch in place of a straight one, though this was really a reversion to seventeenth-century practice.

As John Palmer had foreseen, it was soon possible to reduce the mileage rate paid to the contractors, and for a long while it was as low as a penny a mile (except on some particularly remote and difficult Scottish routes, where twopence was allowed), and the coachmasters not unnaturally urged the Post Office to allow them to carry outside passengers. Extra weight was added to their pleas when the Government imposed an extra duty, based on seating capacity, in addition to the existing carriage tax. The mail-coaches paid no tolls, * as the stages did, but were not relieved of this tax, and quite soon after it was imposed coachmasters were permitted to take advantage of the new position of the guard and to carry one passenger on the box.

When the new-style fore boot came into use a passenger seat for two or three was placed, stage-coach fashion, on the leading edge of the roof; but no passenger seating was allowed at the back, for fear of the guard being overpowered, until the very end of the coaching era when a few of the short-route mails (such as London to Brighton) had a full-width dickey seat with room for two passengers beside the guard, whose portion of the seat was slightly elevated above theirs. At no time did the approved-pattern mail-coaches have a backwards-facing roof seat as the stages did.

Because of this limitation of outside places, and greater strictness about the amount of baggage carried on the roof, the mail-coaches were less likely to overturn than the top-heavy stages; this and the presence of an armed guard wearing royal livery recommended the mails to timorous and elderly passengers as much as their regularity endeared them to the businessman.

The space on the roof occupied on the stage-coaches by the rear seat was reserved on the mails for the guard's impedimenta: his pistol case and blunderbuss, the bag-hook on which the short-distance way-mails were hung and his tool 'budget'. For the guard was mechanic as well as custodian. In addition to having to pass an examination in the three R's, to be of proven good character and accustomed to fire-arms, each guard was sent for a fortnight's training to Vidler's coachworks to learn how the coach was serviced and how to tackle such jobs as shipping the spare pole (slung below or beside the perch) or repairing broken springs or tyres with screw-clamps, and similar running repairs. If a coach became snow-bound or broke down beyond the capacity of the guard's first-aid it was his

* There were some exceptions to this rule, and it seems that at certain periods tolls *were* levied on mail-coaches at some of the London gates.

duty to 'carry forward the mail', for which purpose he usually took the lead horses: so he had to be a competent horseman. In addition to a considerable amount of clerical work it was also his duty to help 'put to' the horses at every change; as the mails ran both night and day this often entailed taking tinder box or coach lamp and rousing horsekeepers from their slumbers in barn or loft. Five minutes were allowed for each change, but as the mail-coach spirit began to work horsekeepers and ostlers took pride in bettering the official time, and it was not uncommon for teams to be changed in ninety seconds. The guard was responsible, of course, for collecting and delivering the mailbags at the different stations, and this was no small labour; for all this work and responsibility the wage of half a guinea a week seems pretty meagre, but clothes were provided and the Post Office did not discourage the giving of tips, which were often on a generous scale. Also, there were rudimentary pension and sick-pay arrangements, and although the work was hard and the pay small the honour of wearing the King's coat was then no small attraction.

Stage-coaches were often rather gaudily coloured and over-adorned and Thomas De Quincey, that great devotee of the mails, wrote: 'Once I remember being on the box of the Holyhead Mail . . . when a tawdry thing from Birmingham, some *Tallyho* or *Highflyer*, all flaunting with green and gold came up alongside of us. What a contrast to our royal simplicity of form and colour in this plebian wretch . . .' The mails were, indeed, rich but sober in their livery of red wheels and running-gear, lower coach panels of deepest maroon, the boots and quarters glossy black, the royal arms emblazoned on the doors and the 'stars' of the four orders of chivalry painted in heraldic colours on the quarters. The words 'Royal Mail' together with the terminal points—London–Leeds—were lettered in gold below the window frames; also in gold or scarlet were the monarch's cipher on the fore boot and the coach number on the hinder one. By contrast the stage-coaches often burst forth in riotous yellow or sky blue, and in addition to the proprietor's name writ large (as the law required) the doors often bore representations of the signs, Blue Boar, Belle Sauvage or Swan with Two Necks, of the inns from which they operated. In addition to the destination signs, the fore and hind boots not only bore the name of the coach, *Magnet*, *Quicksilver*, *Telegraph*, but the intelligence that the vehicle was Patent, Safety or Improved. Tradition dies hard, and it is in the same vein that motor manufacturers brand their wares in flowing chromium script with Automatic, Twin Carburettor or Powerglide.

The highest possible standards of spit-and-polish were maintained on the mail-coaches and the horses matched the equipages in the perfection of their grooming and the effulgence of their trappings: stage-coach turnout emulated but seldom equalled that of the mails.

By modern standards coach travelling was markedly lacking in comfort. The inside passengers sat too upright for ease in an ill-ventilated box, rather lacking in elbow-room (particularly in the 'six inside' vehicles) and with their knees almost touching those of their opposite numbers: those elegant, cross-legged, narrow folding tables (tray-stands, in fact) which the antique trade persistently miscalls 'coaching tables' could never have been erected in any coach known to man. Those who had to ride with their backs to the horses often found the motion very trying. The outside passengers not only ran more risk in an overturn but suffered more discomfort. Their seats, known as gammon boards, were narrow and sparsely padded, the only back rest was an iron rail just above the buttocks and the occupants were exposed to the worst that the English climate could do. In his *Essay* R. L. Edgeworth records more than one occasion when outside passengers died from exposure, and on one particularly bitter night three passengers on one coach reached their destination frozen to death. There were compensations, however, and the 'outsides' enjoyed a commanding view of roads unsullied by concrete kerbing and ill-conceived 'street furniture', and across unspoilt countryside not yet festooned with overhead cables: the very prevalence of dank, grey, rainy days made more pleasurable the rare delight of outside riding on a fine day of warm summer or crisp, bright winter. It is significant that when coaching was revived as a social and sporting pastime in the 1880s the outside seats cost twice as much as the inside ones; exactly reversing the conditions which obtained before the railways came.

It is easy to see that a van-shaped, bus-like conveyance, with all seats inside, could do the work better and many writers advocated such vehicles long before Shillibeer introduced the omnibus to London; but the English public perversely liked their outside seats, as the bus operators soon found. Also the sheer panache of the stage- and mail-coaches, and their undeniable beauty, accounted for a large measure of the glory of the coaching age.

It is impossible to overestimate the effect of the transport revolution of (roughly) 1780–1820; it was even more dramatic in many ways than that which accompanied the successful mechanization of road travel in the early years of this century. It can be illuminated dimly by saying that before the mail-coach era a London businessman writing to Birmingham on Monday could not expect a reply before the close of business on Saturday, but Palmer's innovation ensured that the answer to his Monday letter reached him on Wednesday, as it does today; and within a few years all the cross- and bye-mails were accelerated to integrate with the new fast through-mails.

When Telford made the through mail service from London to Holyhead possible, the mail-coach time for the 261 miles was set at twenty-six hours and fifty-five minutes, which included the time allowed for changing teams twenty-seven times and a meagre forty minutes for meals. This meant that over many of the easier stages the coach ran at an average speed of about thirteen m.p.h., which would have been quite impossible for any vehicle over any road at the beginning of our period. The best of the stage-coaches matched the mails for speed, but it was the wonderful regularity of the latter which fired the public imagination and brought a new concept of punctuality into business affairs.

All this required prodigious organization and is the more remarkable when it is recalled that the only means of communication *was* by mail, and all the many hundreds of letters, directions, demands, way- and time-bills which directed the complicated machine had to be written by hand, and copied by a copying clerk (until James Watt's letter-copying press was invented). A further difficulty which Hasker had to counter when the practical direction of the service came into his hands was that most of the arrangements Palmer and Bonner had made with coachmasters were verbal and tentative. Few written contracts existed, and in his dealings with coach- and horse-keepers Hasker had to steer a difficult course: he had to direct, order, cajole and remonstrate with sufficient force to command a very complex business, knowing that if he drove too hard, the contractors, that most individualistic class of men in a highly individualistic society, would give him the eighteenth-century equivalent of the raspberry.

The problem of getting this great interlocking machine running to time was complicated by the fact that there was no single standard time observed throughout the country. In every sizeable town the local clockmaker kept his shop 'regulator', or precision timekeeper, and the church clock true to Local Apparent Time which he checked by meridianal observation when opportunity offered, making, necessarily, the appropriate correction for the equation of time. The local inhabitants and those responsible for setting the church clocks in near-by villages took their time from this source, but even in a country as small as Great Britain there is nearly half an hour difference in apparent time between east and west coasts. This greatly complicated the business of drawing up and keeping strict schedules.

As strict timekeeping lay at the root of an efficient mail service, each guard was equipped with an official timepiece, which was carried slung over his shoulder in a locked glass-fronted box contained in a leather satchel. This timepiece, with a note of its number and its observed rate of gain or loss, was signed for at the start and finish of each run, and at every post-house or changing station the time by the piece had to be entered in the time-bill and countersigned by an official. The officers at the G.P.O. could therefore pinpoint every stage in a journey where the coach had fallen behind time and interrogate the guard; worse still, from their point of view, the watch prevented guards and coachmen from getting ahead of time in order to spend a few illicit moments snatching an extra drink. Only at the terminal points did officials have keys to the boxes and authority to wind and alter the timepieces: attempts were made, without very much success, to adjust the regulators to make the watches gain or lose in accordance with the variation of apparent time on the east–west journeys.

The coach guards and drivers resented this enforced timekeeping and the snooping it entailed, and the timepieces suffered many curious accidents. Hasker was continually obliged to write in the following vein:

To Mail Guard J. Kelly   *G.P.O. Nov. 11, 1796*
Sir,
On your journey up to Lancaster the Timepiece was very much broke and, it seems, came into Lancaster buckled to the strap-iron behind the coach instead of being buckled to you. In that situation no wonder it was broke—it lays Between you and Johnson and I

will find out the default. Write me every particular you know of it—and write truth.

T.H.

Yet in spite of all these difficulties, those who lived by the mail routes soon came to rely on the passing of the coach rather than the church clock, and used it as we use the wireless signal to set their clocks and watches.

As the roads grew better and better and carriage construction, with particular regard to the iron work, improved it was possible to make the coaches lighter. By 1820 the approved pattern mail-coach scaled only 16 cwt unladen. Stage-coaches were rather heavier, as the bodies had to be stoutly framed to support their loads, but the variety known as post-coaches (run by the proprietors of the posting-houses and having no connection with the mail service) were as light and swift as the mails. McAdam and Telford both lived just beyond the zenith of coaching, which was reached in 1835 in which year 700 mail-coaches and 3,300 stage-coaches were running regularly. This industry employed about 35,000 men as coachmen, guards and horsekeepers; the indirect employment was probably as much again. When it is stated that more than 150,000 horses were needed to draw the coaches, and an unnumbered multitude more in the ancillary services of fodder and dung carting, it can be seen why some economists began to shake their heads and say that if road traffic continued to grow for another thirty years at the same rate as it had done since the turn of the century the entire agriculture of the country would be insufficient to feed the horses let alone the people. Fortunately the steam engine was ready to take over.

CHAPTER EIGHT

Omnibuses

The interest displayed in transport history in recent years has been focused in general upon the mechanical vehicle and in particular upon the private car; upon this aspect a vast flood of material has poured off the presses. Commercial vehicles, however, are of much more significance than private ones, and the motor omnibus has been one of the most potent factors in shaping the modern social structure, particularly in rural areas. Its predecessor, the horse bus, was of equal significance in the nineteenth century, although its influence was necessarily restricted to towns and suburbs.

As with so many vehicles the omnibus was of French origin, a service of eight-passenger *carrosses à cinq sous* having been started in Paris in 1662 by Blaise Pascal with the backing of the Duc de Rouanès. This enterprise was short-lived and despite a half-hearted attempt with a freakish six-wheeled contrivance in England in 1800 no real omnibus service existed between the collapse of Pascal's venture and 1819, when Jacques Laffitte reintroduced the omnibus, now an eighteen-seater, to the Paris scene and made a success of it. Credit for inventing the name goes to a M. Baudry, proprietor of a bathing establishment in the suburbs of Nantes, who provided a vehicle for the convenience of his patrons. This ran at fixed intervals and, if space permitted, took up passengers other than those destined for the bath; to publicize this aspect of his conveyance M. Baudry lifted the name 'omnibus' from the advertisements of a local grocer called Omnès who had caused amusement by painting the slogan 'Omnès Omnibus' above his shop window.

It is often said that the first proper omnibus service in England was established by a Frenchman, but George Shillibeer, though long resident in France, was an Englishman. He had, indeed, served as a midshipman in the Royal Navy before joining Hatchetts of Long Acre to learn the business of a coachbuilder. Then, taking advantage

127

of the popularity of English carriages in France, Shillibeer set up in business in Paris soon after the end of the Napoleonic Wars and became prosperous. Early in the 1820s Jacques Laffitte's success inspired imitators and he determined to quash the opposition by putting into service omnibuses of such superior quality as to put his rivals to shame. The first two improved buses were ordered from Shillibeer, who, having built them and seen how popular they became, decided to sell his business, return to London and start an omnibus service there.

At that time Londoners with no carriage of their own had three choices: they could take a hackney coach or one of the newfangled cabs, the first being expensive, slow and usually dirty, and the second being faster and less expensive but subjecting the passengers to the almost certain hazard of being pitched out head first should the horse fall: they could take one of the short-stage coaches which plied over a few routes, but which were almost as expensive as a hackney coach and very inconvenient, as they did not run to set times, and delayed their passengers *en route*, as they also served as common carriers and had to stop frequently to pick up or deliver parcels. The third choice, accepted willy-nilly by the majority, was to walk.

Shillibeer's first two buses ran from the Yorkshire Stingo at Paddington to the Bank, and the service started on 4 July 1829. It was a route already served by the short-stage coaches (which took three hours to cover the nine miles), and was also the scene of Walter Hancock's experimental steam *chars-à-bancs* service.

The first 'Shillibeers' were drawn by three well-matched bay horses abreast and carried twenty-two passengers, all inside. The fare was one-third of that for inside passengers on the coaches—a shilling full distance or sixpence for the half journey or less. The buses were fresh and gaily painted, and though we might consider the windows (which rattled abominably) too small, and the longitudinal bench seats sparsely upholstered and too narrow, they offered a degree of comfort and cleanliness quite unknown to all but the richer citizens of George IV's London. In addition, the drivers were smart and sober and the nattily uniformed amateur conductors, sons of naval acquaintances of Shillibeer's, were much better spoken and more courteous than most stage-coach men: as a final touch of luxury, magazines and newspapers were provided free of charge. These buses were an immediate success, understandably enough, and soon were earning a hundred pounds a week, each making twelve double journeys a day.

Within a short while the 'gentlemen conductors' who had helped Shillibeer start the service gave way to paid officials: these, too, were smartly uniformed (in blue velvet) and civil, but as the bell-punch system lay in the future they were able to set a pattern, which became all too familiar to bus proprietors, by cheating their employer right and left. More omnibuses were added to the first couple, and fresh routes were exploited, but despite ample evidence of their working to capacity the takings declined. Two of the first official conductors were sacked after they were overheard boasting in their cups that they were easily able to filch ten pounds a week; but Shillibeer did not prosecute.

The first attempt to stop peculation was made when an ingenious workman offered Shillibeer a 'register' which could be concealed below the floor of a bus and actuated by pressure on the tread-plate of the step. By halving the number recorded by the machine (which, of course, increased its tally whether passengers entered or left the vehicle) it was possible to make a reasonably accurate assessment of the number of people carried. Shillibeer bought and fitted one of these devices and agreed to buy more if the inventor would serve as conductor on the fitted omnibus during a trial period. At first all went well, but the solidarity of the proletariat, so esteemed by those progressive intellectuals who have never encountered it except in theory, was put into play. The two discharged conductors, with a number of sympathizers, attacked the bus with the register machine as it stood outside the Yorkshire Stingo one evening, smashed the device to smithereens and half killed the inoffensive inventor.

Shillibeer's first buses had the bodies carried by four longitudinal full-elliptic springs attached to the 'ex-beds' of a conventional perch undercarriage. There were complaints from the newly formed police (who became responsible for licensing hackney and short-stage carriages) that these buses were too big for the city streets, and particularly that the practice of having three horses abreast made them unwieldy. Accordingly, the next batch of 'Shillibeers' were smaller, with seats for sixteen instead of twenty-two inside passengers, but with the driver's box made wide enough to take one passenger on either side of the driver. These new buses were 'perchless', with the springs attached to the axles: the door, as before, was in the back with a platform and hand-grip for the conductor alongside the step by which the passengers entered. Two horses usually sufficed, though on the longer and hillier routes, as they developed, three were sometimes used and, occasionally, four. The three horses were now 'put to' as one leader and two wheelers.

This remained the basic form of the omnibus for some years, though the driver's seat was soon made the full width of the vehicle so as to accommodate two more 'fares' beside the driver. In 1850 a narrow longitudinal seat and footboard were added to the roof, on the offside, on which five extra passengers could perch rather precariously facing the centre of the road. Access to this seat was by a series of narrow tread-plates on the back of the body beside the door, and considerable agility was needed to gain the roof. Although the police frowned upon the practice, the conductors often allowed extra passengers to sit upon the near side of the roof itself, clinging to a strap which ran from front to back, with their heels dangling against the windows which, being of thin glass, were often shattered thereby to the understandable vexation of the 'insides'. This unsatisfactory arrangement eventually gave way to the 'knife-board' or back-to-back seat running along the centre of the roof with a low guard rail around the edge.

It was scarcely possible, and was considered most unseemly, for a woman to clamber on to the roof of a knife-board bus, and a great step forward was made in 1881 when the London Road Car Company introduced the 'garden seat' arrangement for the upper deck with adequate guard rails and a curving staircase wide enough for the most voluminously skirted woman to use without difficulty or impropriety. The staircase and its supporting platform were, at first, at the front of the vehicle with the driver's box carried on a kind of outrigger, but this arrangement was not satisfactory and these Road Car buses were altered by turning the bodies hind-side-before on the underframe and fitting a conventional driver's seat to the leading edge of the roof: this was the direct ancestor of the most usual modern form of double-deck bus with its wide rear platform giving access to the interior by a doorway and to the upper stage by a curved stairway.

In the scope of this book it is impossible to follow in detail the growth of the omnibus business throughout the country, or even in London alone; but this growth was rapid and continuous and the social consequences prodigious. Twenty-five years after Shillibeer's first two omnibuses started work there were nearly a thousand buses in London, and by the end of the century (admittedly in a much larger area) this total had quadrupled. Shillibeer's initial success stimulated imitation within a few weeks, and despite opposition from the short-stage coach proprietors new routes were quickly developed —and more quickly still when the stage-coach owners became bus operators themselves. Some owners competed with Shillibeer on the routes he had established and as, at that time, the buses were generally called 'Shillibeers' (the name 'omnibus' was not well received by the literate and 'bus' was thought a detestable vulgarism) these rival proprietors painted the word 'Shillibeer' on the sides of their buses. To counter this, the originator had painted on each side of his vehicles the legend 'Shillibeer's Original Omnibuses', though this did him little good, as his rivals retaliated by painting their buses exactly the same, but with the word 'Not' in minute letters concealed in the arabesquerie and curlicues with which coach-painters adorned their lettering.

Partly because of the failure of a William Morton whom he took into partnership, and partly because of the growing rivalry, Shillibeer sold his Metropolitan interests in 1834, by which time he was part-owner of sixty buses, six hundred horses and the necessary stabling and accommodation. He started a 'long-distance' service to Greenwich in the belief that the projected London to Greenwich Railway would be abandoned if a good public road service was shown to be operating: this was too optimistic. The railway was opened towards the end of 1835 and Shillibeer's takings dwindled; there was, in fact, room for both services, but, being short of ready money, Shillibeer fell into arrears with his licence fees to the Stamp and Tax Offices, where the officials, instead of accepting his offer to pay by instalments over a period, seized his omnibuses as surety for the debt, thereby making certain that the monies due to the Crown could not be earned and that the business would be bankrupted. The matter was raised in the House of Lords, where it was agreed that Shillibeer had been harshly and stupidly treated; but the promises of compensation were never fulfilled, and Shillibeer set up in business as an undertaker and was soon prosperous again. He devised a new form of hearse and as, by this time, the name 'omnibus' had become acceptable the word Shillibeer became synonymous with a funeral carriage. In auctioneers' language (last refuge of pomposity and bogus latinity, where a coal bucket becomes a *purdonium* and a spittoon a *salivarium*) a hearse is still described as a Shillibeer.

Legally the first omnibuses were classed as short-stage coaches, and an Act of Parliament in 1832 permitted them to pick up and set down passengers in the streets as well as at their terminal and intermediate staging-posts. Another Act in 1838 altered the designation to 'Metropolitan Stage Carriage' and required drivers and conductors to be licensed and to wear numbered badges; the Stamp Office licence number of the bus together with a notice about the maximum permitted number of occupants had also to be prominently displayed. Naturally, towns other than London followed the capital and in most provincial places the licensing and supervision rested with the local council, but in London it was made the business of a department of the police. Though this came about fortuitously, it proved to be a happy accident when motor omnibuses were introduced.

The regulations about the permitted number of passengers were based upon the supposition that a space sixteen inches wide sufficed for an adult human. Alas! theory and practice did not march together; the average Victorian backside was more than sixteen inches across, and quarrels frequently arose as passengers shoved and jostled for place on the longitudinal bench seats. Some broad-bottomed burghers even took to carrying tape measures with them the better to insist upon their legal moiety of posterial space.

It is too readily assumed that traffic jams and road accidents are modern phenomena born of the motor age, but these things are not new. Anarchy reigned in city streets at the beginning of Queen Victoria's reign and the new buses contributed to it; collisions were common and fatalities frequent. After the Act of 1832 was passed to permit taking up and setting down passengers at intermediate points one of the luxuries Shillibeer added to his buses was a check string running centrally along the underside of the roof and communicating with the driver by a large wooden ring through which he slipped an arm. By a pull on the cord, conductor or passenger could signal the driver to pull up, but one of Shillibeer's rivals went one better and fitted two check strings, one either side, and obliged his hapless drivers to wear a ring on either arm. A pull on the left hand string warned the driver to pull up on the normal, or near, side but on feeling a jerk on his right arm he would drive across the traffic for the convenience of a passenger who wanted to get out on the 'wrong' side of the street. It seems odd that such a system should have been allowed in so crowded a town as London; but it became so popular that most companies copied the idea, which was still in use in the 1870s.

The first bus conductors had been notable for their courtesy, but by the 1840s they had become notorious not only for dishonesty but for their bullying incivility and the word cad, * in its pejorative sense, became synonymous with conductor. The larger companies, who worked together in 'associations' to regulate fares and routes on which they agreed not to poach each other's preserves, made great efforts to improve matters, but the 'pirate' operators employed the lowest class of ruffians who did not scruple to cajole passengers (generally female) aboard on the false pretence that they were indeed bound for the destination inquired about, and then, the victim having discovered that she was not being taken to the right destination, refusing to stop the bus until the full fare had been paid. Thomas Tilling was one of the first proprietors to raise standards; partly by his own example of integrity and partly by paying fair wages he did a great deal to make the office of bus conductor as honourable as Shillibeer had intended it to be.

A turning-point in the organization of London's bus services came in 1855 with the formation of the *Compagnie Générale des Omnibus de Londres,* which was a Paris-based, French-financed company, founded to buy and operate the stock and routes of the principal London proprietors. In order not to arouse hostility the *Compagnie* adopted the *nom de guerre* of the London General Omnibus Company, but the secret soon leaked out and provoked considerable opposition. The first buses to bear the name of 'General' began working the Islington and Holloway routes on Monday, 7 January 1856: they had formerly been the 'Favourites', operated by Wilson, whose fifty buses, five hundred horses and one hundred and eighty men passed into the service of the new concern.

The *Compagnie Générale* had planned to bring five hundred buses under their command in the first few weeks, but several proprietors refused to sell and the half thousand was not reached until 1857; in the following year, the French origin of the company having become widely known and bitterly resented, the original concern was

* Originally a diminutive of 'cadet'.

wound up and the London General Omnibus Company, hitherto a mere name, was incorporated as an English joint-stock limited company with a nominal capital of £700,000. English directors predominated on the board and French shareholding in the company dwindled almost to nothing by the end of the century.

Until the amalgamation of all London's public transport services under the London Passenger Transport Board in 1933 the L.G.O.C. was the largest single omnibus operator, but never succeeded in establishing a monopoly. A handful of the old 'independents' remained resolutely independent (Thomas Tilling, J. Manley Birch and the London Road Car Company are names which spring to mind), and one-man-band 'pirates' enlivened the London scene. By the end of Queen Victoria's reign the London General Omnibus Company were working 1,373 buses with approximately 14,000 horses and in the half year ended 30 June 1901 they had carried 101,109,572 passengers over nearly sixteen million route miles.[1]

One of the first actions of the L.G.O.C. was to offer a £100 prize for an improved omnibus; seventy-four designs were submitted, but the judges, though awarding the prize to a coachbuilder called Miller, did not consider any one design worthy of adoption in entirety. Different features from different sources were adopted and it was from this competition that the 'knife-board' form of roof seating came into use, thereby increasing the outside accommodation to fourteen and then to sixteen passengers.[2]

The basic form of the bus, indeed, did not materially alter, though many minor details of springs, axles, windows, seats and ventilators were improved. The first 'garden seat' buses of the London Road Car Company (with the improved staircases) were made very easy to enter and leave by the use of deep-cranked axles which brought the floor (and the centre of gravity) much lower than was usual, but this admirable innovation was too radical and did not survive. There was rather less justification for the railway-like arrangement of springs outside the wheels which the Metropolitan buses sported towards the end of the century. For the first time since Shillibeer's day these very large buses had three horses abreast, but they were not allowed in the City after 10 a.m.

The L.G.O.C. and other companies quickly followed the lead of the London Road Car Company with enlarged mounting platforms, easy stairways and better upper-deck seating; some old 'knife-board'

18 The octogenarian Marquess of Anglesey, 'One-Leg', driving his curricle

19 Shillibeer's three-horse-abreast omnibus of 1829

20 Road Car Company's omnibus of 1881, the first to have a staircase suitable for women passengers

buses were rather unsatisfactorily converted to the new style, but most of them were sold off to provincial operators.

Though we have so far only been concerned with London's buses, the lesser towns and cities were not far behind the capital, and by the end of the century most provincial operators bought or built new buses, not infrequently superior to London's, as local pride and economic factors made the second-hand London bus no longer acceptable. One of the most sensible innovations, the pedal-operated brake, came to London from Glasgow, where James Henderson had fitted driver-controlled brakes to the city's buses some twenty-five years before London followed suit. The brake made the horses' work easier, and the harnessing simpler (as breeching straps round the wheelers' rumps were no longer needed), but threw out of work numbers of poor old men who had previously stationed themselves on hills to put on or take off the drag-shoes.

By the last quarter of the nineteenth century the average bus cost £150 and lasted about twelve years. On a reasonably level route two horses could haul twenty-eight people in a bus at the same speed, but with greater safety, than the much smaller payload had been pulled by four horses in the mail coaches of seventy years earlier.[3] The first major opposition to the bus companies came with the introduction of the street railway from America. The first tramway in Great Britain started work in Birkenhead in 1860, and this was the start of an improvement in urban communication which made further expansion of the bigger towns possible.

In very general terms the cost of horsepower for a tram was half that for a bus of comparable capacity, and if allowance is made for the cost of laying and maintaining the track the tramway still showed an advantage of about one-third. In many places the tramways were set up, or taken over, by the municipalities, which made it possible to finance them at favourable rates of credit. Also, as the trams lent themselves more readily to mechanization than road vehicles, steam-power, compressed air, cable haulage by fixed engines and finally electricity were applied to them, whilst the buses still depended upon horses. This was a further disadvantage, but the demand for all forms of transport continued to grow and the bus services to expand.

The disturbing factor for the bus companies by the end of the century was not so much the competition from municipal trams or suburban electric railways, but the damaging effect of increased traffic upon their horses. As the streets grew more crowded the strain of constant stopping and restarting exacted an ever heavier toll. In 1840 it had been reckoned that a good horse could give seven years omnibus service before being sold for lighter work or slaughter, but fifty years later the working life in London, on average, was only four years. The horses generally used for bus work by this time were mostly Canadian, and they were put to work at five years old. In 1890 the average price paid was thirty pounds, and when it is remembered that a stud of ten horses (twelve in hilly districts) was needed to keep one bus in service it will be seen that the cost of 'horsing' a bus, exclusive of the capital cost of stabling, was not far short of £3,000 in terms of 1969 values.

It will also be seen that with approximately 4,000 omnibuses in use in Greater London by 1900, the inconvenience and cost of removing the droppings of forty thousand horses was sufficient alone to make the bus companies look favourably upon motor traction.

In 1897–8 the first motor omnibus to have been seen in London since the days of Walter Hancock (see Chapter 11) made occasional runs from Marble Arch to Notting Hill. It was a Radcliffe-Ward battery-electric vehicle which was not licensed by the police and which, consequently, carried passengers without charge: it had no outside seats, but was otherwise like a conventional horse bus shorn of its pole and horses. Two years earlier the Electric Motive Power Company had advertised a full-scale double-deck electric bus[4] which seems never to have got further than the drawing-board. The Radcliffe-Ward experiment, though supposedly the forerunner of an extensive fleet for which the promoters had great hopes, also came to nothing. Presumably the occasional runs made during seven months were enough to show that battery-electric traction was far too expensive to compete with the horse.

A year after the electric bus had disappeared London's first licensed motor bus started running from Kennington Park to Victoria Station. The date was 9 October 1899, the projectors were the Motor Traction Co. Ltd and their double-deck vehicles consisted of ordinary horse-bus bodies mounted on Cannstatt-Daimler chassis.[5] Many other companies, including the L.G.O.C. began experimenting with motor buses (petrol engined or steam driven) soon afterwards, but despite the optimism of the designers all these early experiments were of limited mechanical success and quite disastrous commercially.

Limited but encouraging commercial success came to motor-bus operators in rural areas before their citified brethren had done more than earn black looks from their shareholders. Though it is difficult to be certain it is probable that the first profitable motor-bus service was inaugurated by a Somerset cycle engineer, Richard Stephens, who designed and built a most satisfactory motor car in 1897–8. Using enlarged versions of the same design, carrying nine-seated roofed bodies, a scheduled service was satisfactorily operated over hilly country roads in the Clevedon district between 1899 and 1906, when the Stephens buses were supplanted by more modern designs.[6] The Stephens machines had horizontally opposed two-cylinder engines, with steel cylinder liners screwed and brazed into cast-iron heads, of $3\frac{29}{32}$ inches bore by 6 inches stroke which developed about 15 b.h.p. at 800 r.p.m. Though the belt and pulley two-speed primary drive of the Stephens may have looked rather primitive, the chassis details were well thought out, brakes and steering were excellent, and independent front-wheel suspension, forty years ahead of its time, contributed to good handling. Some other rural operators, using more conventional vehicles, also scored reasonable financial success in the first years of the century.

There are three main reasons why small-scale operations could succeed where the bigger town-based operators failed. Country routes entailed less stopping and restarting; the small proprietor or manager working only half a dozen or so vehicles could drive himself part of the time and could find and train men to drive with reasonable mechanical sensitivity; most of these rural services were run with small vehicles, seating twelve or fourteen people usually, and the expense of maintaining the tyres, though heavy, was less crippling than with the bigger buses demanded for town work.

It is difficult for the modern motorist to visualize the magnitude of the tyre problem at the beginning of the century. Pneumatic tyres were essential for speeds of twenty m.p.h. or more, and a motorist who drove carefully in a fairly light car, not too fast, might have 2,000 miles wear from his expensive pneumatics if good fortune attended him; equally he might well have less than half of this meagre mileage. The pneumatic tyre of the time was unable to cope with vehicles weighing more than about thirty-five cwt gross and the solid tyres used on the heavier, slower, vehicles were almost as troublesome and expensive as pneumatics. It is true that they could not puncture, but they could and did stretch, creep, break, fly off the rim and disintegrate in a variety of perverse and expensive ways.

There is plenty of evidence in the motoring journals and technical papers to show the extent of the problem. Solid tyres supposedly capable of carrying a three-ton load for 10,000 miles were found to need replacement after a fifth of the distance, and one motor-bus proprietor wrote in 1902 to say that his figures for a year's working with two fourteen-seater buses showed that the tyre costs were 10*d*. per mile. As the total cost of electric-tram operations was reckoned to be between 11*d*. and 1*s*. per mile it can easily be seen that the motor bus could not compete until the tyre-makers improved their wares— which they very quickly did—and that the *ignis fatuus* of the elastic wheel still attracted hopeful inventors.

Most vehicle designers of the time thought of the internal-combustion engine as a constant-speed machine and, indeed, with hot-tube or trembler-coil ignition, atmospheric inlet valves and single-jet non-automatic carburettors the first motor engines were very inflexible. Control of engine speed by charge-volume throttling was frowned upon as theoretically wasteful and was actually impracticable to a great extent because of the inability of early carburettors to adjust themselves to rapidly changing rates of gas flow. Consequently most engines, particularly those powerful enough for bus work, were not throttled, but tended always to work, load permitting, at peak speed subject to the dictates of a centrifugal governor which cut out the action of the exhaust-valve lifters at a set speed. Broadly speaking, therefore, variations in vehicle speed were only attainable by changing gear, but smooth silent gear-changing with a constant-speed engine, heavy clutch parts and large coarse-toothed sliding gear wheels was quite beyond the skill of the drivers, all of whom were, of course, novices. With the heavy vehicles needed to carry the full-scale bus bodies demanded for town work, this combination of unskilled drivers, inflexible engines and the constant gear-changing in traffic wreaked expensive havoc upon transmission systems.

Some of the bigger companies consequently interested themselves in other forms of propulsion. The battery-electric bus had not been a success, but the Metropolitan Steam Omnibus Company ran a satisfactory service with Clarkson buses which had semi-flash boilers fired by paraffin or naptha. Rather similar steam buses were also worked by the National and Road Car companies as well as by provincial operators. The petrol electric system (a petrol engine driving a dynamo-electric motor combination) also had its attractions, as its low mechanical efficiency was offset by ease of operation and freedom from transmission failures. The London General Omnibus Company's first mechanical venture was made in 1902 with a Fischer petrol-electric bus, of American origin, which ran satisfactorily but failed to win police approval.

The big Tilling concern also started to mechanize and put a fleet of Milnes-Daimlers to work on their Peckham–Oxford Circus route in 1904; this was successful and other routes were mechanized. The Milnes-Daimlers were basically Cannstatt-Daimlers built under licence with certain modifications, the most important being the Iden constant-mesh gearbox, which was easier to operate than the conventional sliding-pinion variety. The Milnes-Daimlers were able to work economically not only on town routes but over some very difficult and hilly country routes, such as the Helston to the Lizard service inaugurated by the Great Western Railway in 1903.[7] In due time, having replaced their Milnes-Daimlers with Leylands, Hallfords and other native makes, the Tilling group set up a motor-manufacturing subsidiary in conjunction with Stevens of Maidstone: this resulted, in 1910, in the Tilling-Stevens petrol-electric heavy-duty chassis, which was the mainstay of many bus operators and municipal authorities for the next twenty years.

By 1904 the tyre bogy was becoming less troublesome and the petrol engine more flexible, thanks to mechanical inlet valves and improved carburettors. Throttle control became practicable and the resultant engine flexibility made gear-changing less hazardous: at the same time the gearboxes themselves were improved and a new race of drivers was developing skill. Transmission breakdowns grew less common and 'conventional' chassis, mostly propelled by four-cylinder vertical engines allied to cone or plate clutches and four-speed gearboxes, reached a high level of reliability and longevity at the hands of such firms as Leyland, Thornycroft, Hallford, Albion, Dennis and many more; nevertheless when the L.G.O.C. made their first big step towards mechanization in 1905 they did so by buying fifty Büssing chassis from Germany and fifty-four De Dion Boutons from France.[8]

To these the Company added native machines, mostly Leylands bought in small batches, for comparison; the results were encouraging and engineering and design departments were set up to work on the Company's own motor-bus design. By the end of 1905 it had been decided to build no more horse buses and work was put in hand to convert stables and equip depots to handle motor vehicles. Early in 1908 the L.G.O.C. amalgamated with the Vanguard and Road Car Companies, both of which had sizeable motor fleets, and a manufacturing subsidiary, the Associated Equipment Company, was established at the Vanguard works in Walthamstow.

Late in 1909 the new company's first bus built to the new Metropolitan Police requirements took the road. This was the L.G.O.C. X-Type, which was satisfactory, but somewhat underpowered; consequently not very many were made and the type was supplanted by the excellent thirty-four-seater B-Type, of which some four thousand were built during the next ten years.

The B-Type bus was so satisfactory and won so much fame as the 'Ole Bill' troop carrier of the Great War that it merits description. It was based upon a rather old-fashioned timber chassis reinforced with flitch plates, suspended fore and aft on semi-elliptic springs, with additional volute springs at the back. It ran on hollow-spoked steel wheels shod with solid tyres (dual at the rear) and was driven by a stout four-cylinder T-head side-valve engine with magneto ignition and thermo-syphon cooling. The engine dimensions were 110 × 140 mm. and at 1,000 r.p.m. it developed about 35 b.h.p.; later versions were enlarged to 115 mm. bore and developed 42 b.h.p. The engine was controlled by the normal type of foot throttle, but was also equipped with a governor acting on a subsidiary throttle to prevent speeding. Transmission was by a cone clutch to a separately mounted four-speed gearbox and then by open shaft to a massive worm-gear, fully-floating live axle. The only unconventional feature of the design was the gearbox, which was of a type favoured by Maudslay with the first and second motion shafts connected not by moveable spur gears but by sprocket wheels and Renold silent inverted-tooth chains. The wheels on the second-motion shaft consequently revolved all the time, but were selectively clutched to that shaft, according to the ratio required, by internal sliding dog-clutches.

This gearbox was not only very quiet running but was proof against the worst that a ham-fisted driver might do: it was possible to make an ugly noise changing gear, but virtually impossible to do any damage, and the old hazard of chips from damaged gear wheels lodging in the bearings and sending them to smash and scatteration, as Mark Twain said, was no more.

The first B-type buses came into service in 1910 and in 1911 motor omnibuses outnumbered horsed ones for the first time in the Metropolitan area. In many small towns without tramways this had happened rather earlier, as conditions were easier, but where tramways existed and were run by the municipal authorities (who were also the licensing authorities usually), motor-bus operators were often refused licenses in order not to jeopardize the profitability of the trams. London did not suffer in this way, as the bus licensing rested with the police. This gave a fortuitous fillip to progress, but sheer commercial considerations also carried weight. By 1909 the costs of motor- and horse-bus working were roughly equal, but by 1912 the running costs, including depreciation, of double-deck motor omnibuses were down below tramway figures—[9] 7d. a mile against 11d. or 1s. At the lowest, horse-bus costs had never fallen much below 1s. 3d. a mile.

In 1913 London's B-type 'buses covered 55½ million miles and lost only 0.02 per cent of scheduled time for mechanical defects.[10] This compared favourably with railway working and would have been beyond the dreams of the most ardent enthusiast for motor traction at the beginning of the century. The horse bus passed away, to be mourned by horse lovers who failed to see that the nasty motor buses they so much deplored had rescued their favourite animals from cruel and degrading slavery.

CHAPTER NINE

Hackney Carriages

Strictly speaking the post-chaise was not a hackney vehicle, but no account of the traffic on eighteenth- and nineteenth-century roads would be complete without some reference to the posting system.

By the time the mail-coach superseded the riding post-boy (at least on those roads good enough for wheeled traffic) the posting system throughout the country had reached a high degree of excellence, and at the posting-houses, which were usually also the principal inns, the well-to-do traveller could be reasonably certain of being able to hire a fresh team of good horses and a willing, competent post-boy (who might be any age between seventeen and seventy) for the next stage of his journey. By 'travelling post' the gentry could make long journeys in the comfort of their own carriages, but with no anxiety about their own 'cattle', and there were well-recognized means of transforming a private coach or town vehicle into a travelling-carriage. The formal 'Salisbury boot', a skeleton affair of wrought-iron stays encased in leather to support the coachman's seat and hammer-cloth, was replaced by a commodious panelled boot able to contain luggage, and the footmen's perch was replaced by a rumble or dickey seat, also with luggage space below it. Shaped flat trunks, called imperials, were fitted to the roof, a drag-staff, or sprag, was attached to the hind axle tree to hold the vehicle from running back on hills, and stout ropes were passed below the coach body, hitched to the standards fore and aft, to prevent disaster in the event of a broken spring. The coachman continued to occupy his box when post-horses were used, exercising nominal control of the wheelers, but the post-boy riding on the near-side lead horse was really the king-pin of the outfit.

The town chariot was similarly converted for travelling with post-horses by being bereft of its coachman's box, which was replaced by a large luggage boot; no coachman was taken and the chariot became

142

a travelling-chaise. Similar vehicles, on a humbler scale, were kept at the larger posting-houses and let on hire. The post-chaise suited the traveller who did not aspire to keep his own coach or chariot, but was able to pay for more comfort and privacy than the stage-coach

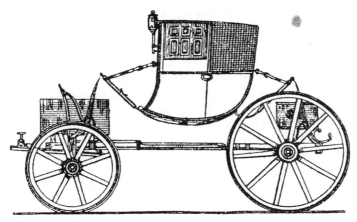

Figure 4 English post-chaise *c.* 1790

could offer. It was inevitably complained that the common post-chaise was a poor shabby affair, battered without and damp within, by comparison with a private carriage; but on the whole the 'po-shays' offered reasonably comfortable and speedy travelling at about three times the price of an inside fare by public coach.

If the complaints about the shabby state of the public chaises were often unjustified, similar grumbles about the hackney coaches, once so spruce and splendid, which plied for hire in London and the other major towns, were well founded. Until the introduction of cabs forced a change, the hackney coach of the late eighteenth and early nineteenth centuries was invariably a pensioned-off private carriage, with all the sadness of decayed gentility about it, sold off to job-master or proprietor who horsed it as cheaply as he could with equally decayed old screws. Dickens wrote of London's hackney coaches:[1]

. . . there is only one coach on the stand now, but it is a fair specimen of the class of vehicles to which we have alluded—a great, lumbering, square concern of a dingy yellow colour (like a bilious brunette), with very small glasses, but very large frames;

the panels are ornamented with a faded coat of arms, in shape something like a dissected bat, the axle tree is red, and the majority of the wheels are green. The box is partially covered by an old great-coat, with a multiplicity of capes, and some extra-ordinary-looking clothes; and the straw, with which the canvas cushion is stuffed, is sticking up in several places, as if in rivalry with the hay which is peering through the chinks in the boot. The horses, with drooping heads, and each with a mane and tail as scanty and straggling as those of a worn-out rocking-horse, are standing patiently on some damp straw, occasionally wincing and rattling the harness; and, now and then, one of them lifts his mouth to the ear of his companion as if he were saying, in a whisper, that he should like to assassinate the coachman . . .

Quite apart from the sad air of decay about the typical hackney coach and its horses, fastidious or timorous people were averse from using them, as, in default of ambulances and police vans, they were used for carrying the sick to hospital, the 'picked-up-dead' to the mortuary and the felon to court or prison; they were all too apt to be verminous and infected. As if this were not enough, the hackney coachmen, as a race, fully deserved their reputation for surly dishonesty and bullying rapacity. In addition to the pleasure of paying a pretty stiff price for a very poor article, the fare was reasonably sure of being overcharged. In the early years of the nineteenth century the hackney-coach pro-prietor had to pay a fee of ten shillings a week for each licence plate, and the drivers, who were paid about nine shillings a week 'retainer', were entitled to all they could get above the fixed scale of minimum charges which were:

> One shilling for the first mile, and sixpence extra for each half mile, or part of half a mile, thereafter. By time and waiting fare, three shillings an hour for the first three hours and two shillings an hour for each additional hour or part of an hour.

The estimation of the distance was a perpetual source of dispute between coachman and fare, and any passenger, particularly any woman passenger, who ventured to question the driver's estimate would be subjected to a torrent of abuse. Most of them paid up, though they knew they were being swindled, and as early as 1825 a contributor to the *London Magazine* wrote:

Is there any valid reason why a hackney-coach should not have a pedometer visible to the unfortunate freight? to be noted on entering, to be noted on exiting, as effectual against fraudulent space as a watch is against fraudulent time, with shillings on the dial plate where there are hours; and where there are minutes, sixpences. It would not cost two pounds, it would save endless altercations, it would save typographing a table of hackney-coach fares, it would save a man's money and temper, and go far towards saving the souls of hackney-coachmen . . . our invention is the best of all possible inventions, and therefore it will not be adopted.

The writer was correct; his invention was re-invented many times until, nearly a century later, it was finally adopted under the name (originally) of the taxameter.

Although a few proprietors took pride in keeping clean coaches, good horses and honest drivers, they were far outnumbered by the other sort. A type of hackney chariot, licensed to carry two (later three) inside and one on the box, was brought into use about 1810. It was occasionally driven from the box, but more commonly the driver rode on the nearside horse; it soon became a popular conveyance and over two hundred were licensed by 1814.[2]

The cabriolet as a private carriage had been popular for some while before it was used in London as a hackney vehicle. It derived from the gig, but was an altogether lighter and more elegant vehicle with (originally) a nautilus-shell-shaped body and a folding leather 'head', as the carriage trade used to call a hood. Both the cabriolet and its larger two-horse cousin, the curricle, were adopted by fashionable men who liked to drive themselves, and such well-known dandies as Count D'Orsay and Charles Dickens were cabriolet fanciers, whilst both the Duke of Wellington and the Marquess of Anglesey still drove their curricles when in their eighties. In 1805 Messrs Bradshaw and Rotch were licensed to operate nine hackney cabriolets on condition that they never entered the area bounded by the 'Bills of Mortality'* in which the established coach proprietors

* 'Bills of Mortality': records of deaths published at regular intervals for the cities of London and Westminster and certain of the ancient 'liberties', from the sixteenth century on. The expression 'Within the Bills' to signify the geographical area covered by the Bills, rather than their contents, was still current in the early nineteenth century.

had a monopoly: despite this limitation the established hackney coachmen resisted the innovation with all the venom displayed by their present-day counterparts to the 'minicabs'.

It was not until nearly twenty years later, in April 1823, that David Davies was licensed to work twelve hackney cabs, of a new form, 'Within the Bills', and from that moment the days of the old hack coach were numbered. Apart from their inability to ply in central London, there had been two objections to the original hackney cabriolets: there was room for only one fare and he was obliged to sit beside the driver; in the days when that horrible euphemism for the working class, 'the great unwashed', had some validity this was a real drawback. Also, if the horse fell, a common occurence, when going at any speed the passenger could fairly depend upon being pitched out head first.[3] Because of this, and because of the difficulty of climbing in and out, the cabs were fit only for the young and agile; but they had never lacked custom as they were fast, smart and the fares were a third less than those for a hackney coach—there being only one horse.

The first objection was removed in the new Davies cabs as the driver was accommodated on an odd little dickey seat, outside the vehicle, between the off-side wheel and the body panel. Two 'fares' could now be carried, they were removed from contact with the driver, a hinged leather apron kept wind and rain off their legs and leather curtains could be drawn across the front of the 'head' in really bad weather. Although the hazard of being pitched out was not abolished, these new cabs were even more popular than the earlier type, and the initial dozen grew to 150 in nine years. In 1832 the hackney-coach proprietors were empowered to transfer their licences to cabs, and within another ten years two-wheeled hackneys out-numbered the four-wheeled variety.

Designers were concerned to remove the risk of being thrown out. Three men, in particular, Bulnois, Hansom and Chapman, worked upon the principle of using large wheels mounted either on short axle arms attached to the sides of the body framing, or on a deep-cranked axle passing below the floor, so as to bring the bottom of the body close enough to the ground to remove the danger of tipping too far when the horse went down. Small safety wheels on curved arms were also tried. The Bulnois cab was the first to be adopted, in 1831; this had the door in the back, seats for two passengers sideways-on to the direction of travel and the driver's seat on the front of the roof. When the horse fell the passengers in a Bulnois, or back-door cab, were safe enough, but the driver was usually dislodged.

Joseph Aloysius Hansom's cab of 1833 was a curious vehicle quite

Figure 5 Hansom's patent cab in its original form

unlike that which made his name a household word. It was carried on 7 ft. 6 ins. diameter wheels mounted on short axle arms attached to the framing which was arranged outside the body panels. The driver sat in front, on top of the roof, with window openings on either side of his footrest, and two low doors and steps one either side of the horse's rump. There were no windows, but wooden 'tambour' shutters could be pulled down from roof to door. The great size of the wheels made the absence of springs relatively unobjectionable.

Edward Bulnois modified the Hansom cab by using rather smaller wheels running on a deep-cranked axle, and some of this type of

Hansom plied for hire. Two years later a company was formed to exploit Hansom's 'Patent Safety Cabriolet', but before the concern was well under way a very much better form of safety cab was patented by John Chapman, who was founder and Secretary of the Safety Cabriolet and Two-wheel Carriage Company. The company owning Hansom's patent saw how much superior Chapman's design was to their own; they bought out their rivals and put an initial fleet of twenty Chapmans to work. These were, in all essentials, the 'hansom' cabs which survived for the next seventy years, but because so much publicity had been given to the Hansom patent the new cabs were called by that name instead of by the name of their designer.[4]

The principal difference between what we might call Chapman-Hansoms and Bulnois-Hansoms was that the cranked axle passing below the body was abolished, and the bodywork was cut away and reshaped so that a straight axle could pass directly below the passengers' seat. This allowed room for suspension on three semi-elliptic springs arranged Dennet-fashion. The driver's seat was moved from the front to the back, which gave the driver more security against being thrown out and at the same time allowed his weight, well aft of the wheel centres, to balance the passengers, whose weight came just forward of the centre line.

Changes made to the hansom cab during the next sixty years were only of detail; those made on the Forder-built Shrewsbury and Talbot cabs included the rubber tyres already mentioned, and refinements such as a folding window to fill the space between apron and roof, larger side windows, interior mirror, ashtrays and so forth. The hansom became London's most popular form of semi-public transportation, and was used in many other cities both at home and abroad. It was considered improper for young, unmarried women to ride in hansoms, and it was supposed to be social death for a young woman to ride in a hansom with a young man; though, indeed, they were not unchaperoned, as any tender conversation, or squeezing of the hand (or worse), was liable to be interrupted by the opening of the trap-door in the roof to admit the driver's bloodshot eye and beery voice asking 'Where now, Guv'nor?'

The same David Davies who introduced the cabriolets of 1823 also produced the four-wheeled 'Clarence' cabs in 1835 which, as related in Chapter six, inspired Lord Brougham to have a private carriage of the same design. Similar four-wheelers, or 'growlers', soon appeared in the provinces, but in the smaller country towns and villages a vehicle miscalled a 'fly' was generally used as a hackney. This was a one-horse, four-wheeled carriage which could never quite make up its mind whether it was a stunted landau or an overgrown victoria.

The idea of a fare-registering device was mooted many times after the notion was originally put forward in 1825, and a number of instruments were made and tried, but the outcry from the drivers at any suggestion of regulating their roguery was so loud that no individual proprietor dared adopt the innovation. In 1899 a syndicate was formed to operate 'taxameter' cabs and six were put to work; it was proposed to extend the system to all London hackneys, and three hundred men signed on the syndicate's payroll when it was announced that they would be guaranteed two guineas a week and a percentage of the takings. The Cab drivers' Union then declared the Syndicate 'black', thereby blowing the gaff on their contention that their members, on average, took home less than thirty-five shillings a week, and the project was abandoned. It was not until the motor cab became a commercial proposition that Londoners were protected from the notorious swindling of their cabbies; but the licensing authorities in some of the provincial centres were not to be intimidated by threat of strike action, and taximeters, to use the modern spelling, were adopted in Manchester, Leeds, Liverpool and Bradford before the nineteenth century was out.

The first motor cabs, indeed, antedated the adoption of the taximeter, as a fleet of electric cabs was put to work in London towards the end of 1897. They were built to the design of Walter Bersey and worked by the London Electric Cab Company, which was an offshoot of the syndicate set up by the financier, H. J. Lawson, to monopolize the motor industry in Great Britain.

Electric cabs in ones and twos had already been tried in Paris, but the London venture was the first attempt on a big scale. The cabs passed the fairly stringent requirements of the Metropolitan Police Hackney Carriage inspectorate, and thirty-six were on the road by March 1898; a further forty-one were built, but it is doubtful whether more than sixty were ever available for use simultaneously, because, ambitious though the scheme was, it must be said that the cabs were a total failure both mechanically and commercially.[5]

In order to reduce development costs Bersey used as many existing components as possible, and the design, in consequence, was very much a 'thing of shreds and patches'. The steering-gear, for example, was an adaptation of an ordinary centre-pivoted fore-carriage, although Ackermann steering was already well established

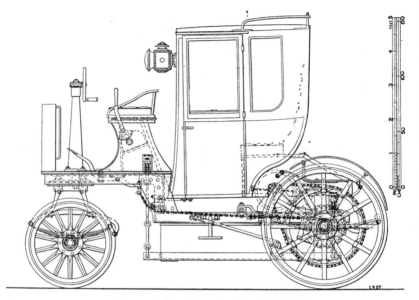

Figure 6 London electric cab 1898

for mechanical vehicles; this resulted in considerable waste of space, and although the vehicles were more than twelve feet long the coupé bodies only had room for two fare-paying passengers. Also the battery boxes only cleared the ground by nine inches but the cab-roofs were nearly ten feet above ground level and, worst of all, the construction was so clumsy that the cabs weighed more than two tons, which was altogether too much for their driving-chains and sprockets, and for their narrow solid rubber tyres which were an endless source of trouble and expense. The jolting of such heavy vehicles on solid tyres wreaked havoc on the 80 volt, 150 amp/hr batteries, which were made up of forty E.P.S. cells. It had been expected that the batteries would last three years, with renewal of the negative plates every eighteen months, but in practice it was found that they

21 Lord Brougham's brougham, 1838

22 Forder-built improved hansom cab c. 1890

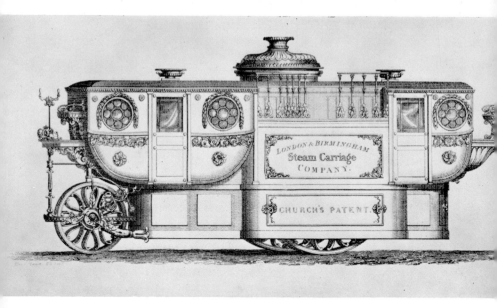

23 Artistic license: an advertiser's dream or engineer's nightmare

24 Hancock's *Enterprise* from a contemporary and almost accurate painting by W. Summers

did not last six months, and the battery suppliers had to revoke their maintenance contract. Also, the 3 h.p. Lundell motors could do no better than drive such heavy creatures at about 7 m.p.h. on the level (9 m.p.h. had been estimated, but could only be achieved with brand new batteries and motors), consequently the 'humming birds', as they were nicknamed, were easily outpaced by the hansoms whose drivers made a point of hurling abuse at the electric-cab 'fares' as they went past.

The big mistake, commercially, was that the Cab Company ignored the advice of leading electricians to install their own generating plant, and contracted to buy current at an apparently advantageous price from the Deptford Electric Light and Power Company. This was alternating current, and as rectifying valves and transistors had not been invented the only way to convert it to direct current, for battery charging, was by using A.C. motors to drive D.C. generators: the electrical and mechanical losses involved inflated the cost of the 'cheap' current by 150 per cent by the time the batteries were charged.

After running with constant transmission and tyre failures for six months the cabs were withdrawn for modification, and the owners did what they should have done initially and installed their own steam engine and generators. The 'humming birds' reappeared, painted black all over instead of black and yellow and fitted with stronger driving chains, on Queen Victoria's eightieth birthday on 24 May 1899; but within a short while they were again in trouble and the world's first motor-cab company was bankrupted in March 1900. They had, at least, provided a good example of what *not* to do.

Only in London was it necessary for motor cabs to comply with stringent regulations which not only covered the day-to-day roadworthiness and cleanliness of the vehicle but mechanical details, such as the radius of the turning circle, and such matters as the width of the doors, the stuffing of the seats and the covering of the floors. All London motor cabs, from the original landaulets to the modern saloons, have been unique in having no passenger's seat beside the driver, and the large amount of luggage space thus afforded has always been a useful feature. Some other cities, notably Glasgow, have now adopted the London-type of taxi, but in general the hackney-carriage requirements of most provincial towns were met by licensing ordinary motor cars for hackney work, with or, without meters or the right to 'ply for hire' in the streets according to local usage. Cars were consequently available for contract or short-term hire in many places before the capital again had a motor-cab fleet after the failure of the electrical experiment.

A number of manufacturers produced motor cabs in ones and twos, to meet police requirements, very early in this century, and the first petrol cabs to ply regularly for hire in London were Rationals designed and made by the old-established coachbuilders, Cockshoot and Company. The Rationals were sound machines with large two-cylinder horizontal under-floor engines driving through a patented form of constant-mesh gear and single chain to a live axle. An unusual, but very sensible, feature was that the steering-column, control pedals and driver's seat were on the centre line of the chassis, which allowed room for two large sliding doors behind and to either side of the driver. The back seat was wide enough for three and a cricket seat accommodated a fourth 'fare' who sat with his back to the partition separating him from the driver's back.

Although these cabs were quite satisfactory, the firm did not continue with motor manufacture after making about half a dozen of them, and about twenty private cars on similar chassis. Other firms, such as Argyll, Belsize, and Humber, after turning out two or three cabs, found their private-car business in need of all the available factory space, and no cab company was willing to place a big enough order for cabs to make a special department profitable. One of the oddest confections came from Vauxhall in the shape of a two-cylinder motor hansom, complete with driver's controls and seat outrigged from the back of the roof in hippomobile fashion. One trembles to think of the number of corners the steering connections and other controls had to go round before performing their functions, but fortunately this monstrosity never plied for hire.

It was clear that making or operating motor cabs in penny numbers would never do, and in 1907 a syndicate was formed (it included members of the Du Cros family who controlled the Dunlop Tyre Co.) to launch and operate a fleet on a big enough scale to justify setting up repair and body-building depots. It was found that the two-cylinder Renaults, used so successfully for taxi work in Paris, would meet the specifications laid down by the police and an initial fifty chassis were imported and fitted with English bodywork. They started operations in 1908, were immediately successful, and the fleet was increased threefold in the first year. There were three reasons for this satisfactory outcome: firstly, that the Type AX Renault chassis was invincibly reliable and long lived; secondly, the organization was well managed and adequately financed and finally the motor cabs were fitted with taximeters. Even the most rigid die-hards soon came to accept that the affront to their finer feelings inherent in riding in 'one of those horrid motors' was a small price to pay for freedom from the cheating and bullying the London cabbies had enjoyed for so long.

The London taxi fleet grew very quickly, other companies were formed, and many owner-drivers took to the new mode. A number of native manufacturers made cab chassis in small numbers, but on the whole French (or Anglo-French) vehicles dominated the London taxi trade for nearly thirty years. The Renaults were joined by Charrons, which looked very similar and were built by an English company which had bought Fernand Charron's manufacturing rights when the original Charron, Giradot and Voight concern was wound up; but gradually the 'Unic' outnumbered all others. This was an admirable four-cylinder vehicle designed by Georges Richard in 1908 expressly to conform to Metropolitan Police specifications. Many of the pre-1914 cabs gave more than twenty years' continuous service and were still able to pass the very strict annual test of roadworthiness.

Writing in 1902 about the failure of the electric cabs, H. C. Moore said: 'Apparently the hansom cab has every prospect of retaining its popularity for another sixty years.' When only ten years of the sixty had passed motor cabs outnumbered hansoms by more than two to one.

CHAPTER TEN

'With Steam to do the Horses' Work'

During the reigns of King George IV and King William IV experiments with steam carriages were so numerous and so nearly reached commercial success that many people almost believed the Jeremiahs who cried that the horse was doomed to extinction, and some unknown versifier (allegedly Thomas Hood) was moved to pen the following effusion:

> Instead of journeys, people now
> May travel on a Gurney,
> With steam to do the horses' work
> By Pow'r of Attorney.

After this optimistic start the poet (if such he can be called) struck a gloomy note with:

> Tho' with a load
> It may explode,
> And you'll find yourself quite undone;
> Travelling fast to Heav'ns Gates
> Instead of down to London.

There is a very great deal of confusion and contradiction about the steam coaches of 1820–40. Seventy years ago most writers would have agreed with H. C. Moore's account of Hancock's experiments, in his *History of Omnibuses and Cabs*, which he concluded by saying that Hancock's steam omnibuses were by no means so satisfactory as the inventor tried to show, and that the turnpike trustees, by levying punitive tolls on steam carriages, really bestowed a benison upon him by enabling him honourably to abandon the project and 'pose as an injured person'.

On the other hand, modern writers who deal with the history of motor vehicles generally attribute to the steam carriage designers

154

and speculators far more success than they achieved. They are too readily deceived by the well-known prints of spanking, glossy steam coaches, bowling through picturesque country, laden with happy, smiling ladies and gentlemen, all impeccably clad in the very 'glass of fashion and mould of form' with never a ruffle or a feather stirred by the velocity of their progress. In most instances these scenes were imaginary, and the vehicles depicted were mere artists' impressions which formed part of the speculators' attempts to raise capital for the companies they hoped to float.

Many inaccurate statements have been made about specific steam carriage operations, and these are endlessly repeated. For instance, modern works on automobile history almost without exception assert that Sir Goldsworthy Gurney established a steam-coach service between London and Bath and that his coaches made the journey at an *average* speed of 15 m.p.h. This scarcely comes within shouting distance of the truth, which is that Gurney essayed to drive *one* of his steamers from London to Bath and back, but was frustrated on the outward journey by a breakdown so serious that the machine ignominiously finished the trip behind a team of horses. According to Gurney's own account the breakdown was trivial and affected only the claw-clutch by which the second driving wheel was coupled to the axle when necessary, but independent evidence belies this. It is probable, though not certain, that that vulnerable feature, the cranked driving-axle, had fractured, but in due time the damage was made good. On the return to London the carriage covered the eighty-four miles between Melksham and Cranford Bridge in ten hours; if due allowance is made for ten halts to take on water and coke the running time for this trip was commendable, and some stretches of a mile or more *were* covered at 15 m.p.h. This is far removed from the myth of a regular steam-coach service operating at a scheduled pace of 15 m.p.h. for the entire journey.

This is not to decry the efforts of many ingenious and painstaking pioneers who, in the twenty years before Queen Victoria came to the throne, very nearly succeeded in bringing about the road-transport revolution which was, in fact, delayed until the twenty years which followed her death. Their failure is often attributed solely to discriminatory legislation and prohibitive toll-charges, but other factors must be taken into account.

One of the difficulties in the way of making an accurate assessment of this first automobile era lies in the lack of precise contemporary evidence. There is ample material but little information. There are, for example, scores of newspaper accounts of steam-carriage trials, mostly laudatory, but these almost always resulted from an invitation to a journalist or newspaper proprietor to participate in a trial trip (and, most probably, a little preliminary junketing) conducted over a relatively short stretch of reasonably good road. Needless to say the writer would be:

> To their virtues very kind,
> To their faults a little blind.

and it is almost invariably said in these reports, for example, that 'the carriage made no noise', but from the very nature of the vehicles with their iron-tyred wheels, and the nature of the roads, we know that even if the machinery were silent (which it was not) the noise must always have been considerable and often excessive.

In many passages these newspaper accounts display, naturally enough, total ignorance of things mechanical, and therefore if some breakdown occured during the trial it was easy enough for the demonstrator to pass it off as a 'trifling mishap to some secondary part of the mechanism' even if something as vital as a crankshaft or driving-axle had snapped.

Nor are the writings of the steam-carriage designers themselves of as much value as one might expect. Many of them contributed fairly extensively to the *Mechanics' Magazine* and similar publications, and some of them published pamphlets dealing with the subject which very often included the most enthusiastic of the newspaper notices; but technical information is disappointingly sparse.

The best-known engineer-authors in the field were Sir Goldsworthy Gurney, Colonel Maceroni and Walter Hancock, but most of the literary efforts of the first two were devoted to self-justification or vilification. Gurney's pamphlet is wholly concerned with arguing, with great ability and justice, that the substitution of mechanical for animal power would benefit the country, and, with very much less justice, that he was the first and only person to have brought the substitution within the bounds of practical realization. Maceroni's writings do give some meagre information about his steam carriages, but they are primarily devoted to proving that all other steam-coach designers and promoters (with particular reference to Gurney) were quacks, rogues, puffers and imposters. So energetically was abuse hurled that it is tempting to conclude that if the powers of vituperation of these engineers had been matched by corresponding mastery of their craft and commercial skill a thriving mechanical carriage industry would have been well established before 1840.

Walter Hancock's *Narrative*[1] is more sober and factual than those of his rivals, but even here there is not enough technical information to satisfy the historian. It would be impossible to make an accurate reproduction of any of Hancock's vehicles from the information and drawings contained in his own account of them.

Since the time of Mother Shipton's prophecy that 'Carriages without horses shall go', and doubtless before it, philosophers had speculated upon different forms of artificial locomotion. These speculations began to encroach on the realms of practicality when scientists of the calibre of Sir Isaac Newton and Denis Papin considered the question. Newton's projected steam carriage was little more than a boiler on wheels which was supposed to propel itself by the reaction of steam issuing from a backwards-pointing jet, but it was at least provided with steering and steam-control levers under the command of the 'coachman', whereas many of the nineteenth-century designers separated the functions of steersman and engineman.* Until fresh evidence comes to light it is now accepted that the first full-scale road vehicles to move by artificial means were the steam trucks built by Joseph Cugnot in Paris between 1765 and 1770. The second of these ran with a fair degree of reliability and has been preserved to show that it clearly established two important principles; firstly, that a non-condensing engine relying entirely on the expansive force of steam under pressure, provided ample power in a small enough space, and secondly that the adhesion of a single driving-wheel was sufficient to draw a weight of some four tons without difficulty.

The genesis of Cugnot's trucks corresponds nearly enough with the start of our period, and with James Watt's improvements to the Newcomen-type of atmospheric steam engine. It would be pleasant to record that the man who did so much to forward the mechanization of industry also contributed to the success of mechanical road

---

* As late as 1894 an agricultural engineer named Soames built a light steam wagonette on which it is the duty of the engine-man to shut off steam and apply brakes if, in the intervals of stoking, he chances to observe that the steersman is about to run into something.

transport, but although Watt sketched some rather hazy proposals for steam-carriage machinery (and secured a patent), his efforts were largely directed to making sure that if he did not make a steam carriage nobody else should.

Watt was repeatedly urged by Erasmus Darwin, Dr Small and others to press ahead with a steam carriage, but at the time of their correspondence with him (1770–80) he treated the matter as of purely theoretical interest and concluded, not unreasonably, that technology was not advanced enough to make it worth while to pursue the project in earnest.

As technical resources improved his attitude to other inventors hardened and can only be ascribed to jealousy. As is well known, he disapproved of, and tried to stop, his assistant, William Murdoch, from following up his most promising steam-carriage experiments; and when he heard from Dr Small that a London linen draper named Moore had been granted a patent for a steam carriage he wrote: 'If linen-draper Moore does not use my engine to drive his chaises he cannot drive them by steam. If he does I will stop him. I suppose by the rapidity of his progress and puffing he is too volatile to be dangerous.'[2] Watt's hostility to steam-carriage designers was ultimately carried to the point where he had a covenant written in to the lease of Heathfield Hall, the house to which he retired in old age, stipulating that: 'no steam carriage should on any pretext be allowed to approach the house'.[3]

Watt realized that his atmospheric engine with its bulky separate condenser and air pump and the other necessary appurtenances was much too large and heavy for locomotive purposes; he was fully alive to the advantages of using steam under pressure (with or without a condenser to improve efficiency according to the nature of the job), and the expansive use of steam was covered by his patent of 1769. In the rather ill-defined proposals he threw out for steam-carriage machinery he envisaged working at 25 p.s.i., which was, by his standards, very high pressure. Yet he remained convinced that such a pressure was dangerously impractical (his condensing engines operated at about 4–6 p.s.i. above atmospheric pressure), and when other engineers demonstrated that his fears were unjustified his jealousy was aroused. Hence his disparagement of Trevithick, Hornblower, Stephenson and others who developed the high-pressure engine, and his opposition to the idea of the steam coach which he knew could only succeed if high-pressure engines were used.

Watt's steam carriage specification included the rocking-beams and sun-and-planet motion which he persisted in using in order to avoid paying royalties on the normal crank which was still, at that time, protected by a patent of rather dubious validity. Partly to offset the weight of all this, he envisaged a hooped wooden boiler with an internal copper firebox. Had it ever been made, this must have been a triumph of the cooper's art, but although most of Watt's steam-carriage ideas were impractical he did design a three-speed variable ratio transmission which was of great merit. It is often said that this was of the sliding gear-wheel variety which formed so notable a part of Emile Levassor's immortal design of 1891 and of which he is alleged to have said *c'est brutal mais ça marche*; but Watt's 'gearbox' was more advanced and less brutal than Levassor's. He specified a constant-mesh three-speed system by spur gears arranged so that those on the second-motion shaft could revolve freely on it or be selectively 'clutched' to it as needed by a sliding feather or elongated key, actuated by a suitable collar and forked yoke. This type of constant-mesh gearing was revived for motor-car work, and is to be found, for example, on some of the M.M.C. cars of 1898–1902.

Watt's specification for steam-carriage machinery was covered by patent in 1784, some fifteen years, that is, after Cugnot's moderately successful demonstration and seventeen more years were to elapse before the first practicable, full-scale, English road steamer made its bow. During this period at least twenty different men dreamed dreams and drew plans for steam carriages, and it is notable that the majority of these speculators were not engineers. From three of them, with practical knowledge of steam engineering, came working models which carried the idea of the horseless vehicle nearer to reality.

One of these models was constructed by William Symington, designer of the world's first practicable steamboat, in 1786. The drawings of this contrivance, which have been reproduced in many histories of engineering, show a vehicle of unwieldy length carrying an elegant coach-body (complete with sword case) supported on springs above the perch and with a horizontal boiler at the rear. The engine had two horizontal cylinders, with the piston rods passing through stuffing-boxes at both ends and linked by chains passing over guide pulleys in such a way that the outward stroke of one piston caused its fellow to be drawn inwards. The outer extremity of each piston rod was furnished with rack teeth which engaged a spur wheel on the back axle: the two spur wheels were mounted on ratchet clutches and the to-and-fro motion of the rack rods was thus to be converted into continuous rotary motion of the axle. Nineteenth-century historians pointed out that this arrangement could never have worked satisfactorily except at very slow speeds, but a more serious defect went unremarked. Steam pressure was very low, and the chief impetus was provided by atmospheric pressure acting on the inward strokes, yet the condenser was no more than a small tank of cold water into which the cylinders exhausted. After only a few strokes this must have become too hot to permit further condensation and it was probably this which caused young Symington (he was only twenty-three at the time) to abandon the project, despite encouragement from the faculty of Edinburgh University; although the ostensible reason he gave was the difficulty of arranging relay stations for fuel and water which would be essential for commercial operation.

William Murdoch experimented with his steam-locomotive model some five years before Symington, but where the Symington could not have worked satisfactorily if produced to full scale Murdoch's little road locomotive had all the elements needed for success. All the complications of condenser and air pump, sun-and-planet-motion and other features of Watt's engines were done away with and, as Fig. 7 shows, the simple little high-pressure engine acts directly on the hind axle. Although Watt disapproved of the experiments, he and Boulton were so anxious to avoid losing Murdoch's services that the former proposed to allow him: '. . . an advance of £100 to enable him to prosecute his experiments, and if he succeeded within a year in making an engine capable of drawing a post-chaise, carrying two passengers and the driver at four miles an hour, it was suggested that he should be taken as partner into a locomotive business for which Boulton and Watt were to provide the capital'[4]. Nothing, however, came of this and it fell to Richard Trevithick to make the first full-scale steam vehicle to run on English roads.

Like Symington and Murdoch, Trevithick had experimented with models before starting to make his first road locomotive in November 1800. The job took nearly a year, and was mostly carried out in John

Tyack's workshop in Camborne, though the heavier lathe work was done by Andrew Vivian (who became Trevithick's partner later) and the boiler plates and some other special parts were cast at Coalbrookdale.

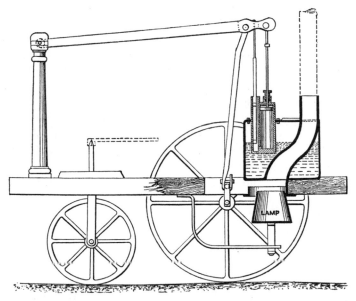

Figure 7 Murdoch's working model road locomotive, 1784

Trevithick's road steamer made its first trial run on Christmas Eve 1801, and succeeded in climbing Camborne Beacon with seven or eight men, in addition to 'Cap'n' Trevithick, clinging on as best they could. For the contrivance was in no sense a steam carriage, but very much a 'road locomotive' made, in effect, by modifying one of Trevithick's standard high-pressure engines, mounting it on wheels and furnishing it with a platform in front for the intrepid conductor to stand on whilst he operated the steering and steam-cock handles, and stoked the return-flue cylindrical boiler. A similar platform behind carried a large feed-water tank and allowed space for the engineer (and one or two others), who tested the water level in the boiler by means of try cocks, and operated the feed-water pump as necessary. The boiler had a lever safety valve, set to blow off at just over 60 p.s.i., and the single, vertical, cylinder was recessed into it and gave motion via outside connecting-rods to crank-pins on the hind wheels.

The machine was far from perfect; the boiler was inadequate and despite Trevithick's innovation of using the exhaust steam to force the fire by a suitable blast pipe in the chimney, it was not possible to maintain full steam for long. Also, in order to provide a reasonably low gear ratio the driving wheels-were too small to cope with the bad roads of the period. The steering arrangements left a good deal to be desired, consisting merely of a lever attached to the centre-pivoted front axle and on one of the trial trips the handle was jerked from Vivian's hands and the machine overturned. Nevertheless, it ran well enough to encourage Vivian to take partnership with Trevithick in a project to make road steamers commercially, and in addition to the exhaust blast pipe two more of Trevithick's innovations were included in the design; these were an efficient tubular feed-water heater and a fusible safety plug in the crown of the firebox.

On 24 March 1802 Trevithick and Vivian were granted a patent for an improved steam vehicle which had more of the carriage and less of the machine shop about it. During the remainder of the year the mechanical parts for a carriage on this new plan were made and tested at Camborne; they were then sent by sea to London, where they were assembled and fitted with a carriage body in Felton's coach-works in Leather Lane. This was Trevithick's celebrated 'London Carriage', which won its designer an honourable place in automobile history and lost him a lot of money.

The well-known engravings of the London Carriage clearly owe much to artistic licence. There seems to be no way in which passengers might reach the interior of the carriage; there are no water tanks or fuel bunkers visible; the boiler seems remarkably small; many of the bearings are supported only by the atmosphere and the steering arrangements look more than a little hazardous. Nevertheless, sufficient is known of the mechanical details to show that Trevithick had the root of the matter in him. The 'chassis' was of wrought iron with its two central longitudinal members serving also as guide bars for the forked piston rod. The single cylinder was horizontal and was recessed into the boiler in Trevithick's usual fashion, and a large flywheel was keyed to the offside of the crank-shaft, which also carried spur gears meshing with corresponding gear wheels on the unsprung hind axle. It has been argued that this gearing was only variable in the sense that it could be altered according to the speed or power required, in much the same way that many motor manufacturers offer different final-drive ratios to choice. The

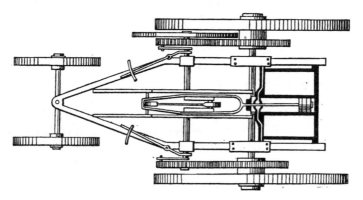

Figure 8 Plan view of Trevithick's 'London' steam carriage

1802 Patent Specification certainly supports this interpretation, but the plan-view drawings of the machine clearly show arrangements for altering the gear on the road (though not whilst in motion).

The crankshaft gears, of different diameters and tooth numbers, meshing with correspondingly different gears on the axle, were apparently free to revolve upon the shaft, but could be selectively 'clutched' to it by moving suitable control levers, one either side of the chassis, which shifted movable collars each with a long projecting arm which could thus be made to bear upon, or to pass clear of, a stout pin projecting from the periphery of the adjacent gear wheel. This contrivance allowed the gear ratios to be changed, but as the final-drive gears and the hind wheels were apparently fixed to the rear axle with no similar 'declutching' device there was no differential action. The disadvantages of the unsprung axle were in a great measure compensated by making the driving-wheels ten feet in diameter, and the carriage seems to have been remarkably reliable. It made several journeys in and around London, at speeds up to ten miles an hour; it was enthusiastically described in the Press, it was driven several times through such crowded thoroughfares as Oxford Street and Tottenham Court Road to show that it was under perfect control, but Trevithick and Vivian could not arouse any financial interest in it. Towards the end of 1804 the carriage was dismantled and the engine and boiler sold for use in a hoop-rolling mill, a duty they performed admirably for many years.

Having invented many important improvements to the steam engine, and having built this very promising road carriage and the world's first steam railroad locomotive, Trevithick spent his last years in poverty and died in debt.

Before Trevithick began work on his first road steamer he demonstrated to a sceptical acquaintance that a loaded wagon could be moved uphill, without horses, merely by having men turn the wheels by hauling on the spokes. Quite why this obvious fact required demonstration is not clear, as many a carter must have helped his struggling beast in this fashion, and the expression 'put your shoulder to the wheel' had long since been in common use. Yet it was an article of faith amongst many 'scientific' men that a carriage could not be moved by applying artificial power to turn the wheels which must inevitably, they said, slip without propelling the vehicle.

Despite its obviously shaky foundation, which is comparable to the soothing belief, still current in the writer's childhood, that a man who fell from a high place would know no fear and feel no pain, as he would surely be dead before striking the ground, and despite the demonstrations of Cugnot, Trevithick and others, the existence of this fallacy influenced several inventors (many of whom should have known better) to design steam vehicles propelled by artificial legs. With metallurgical knowledge in its infancy, with no such thing as a standard screw thread, with few power-driven forging-hammers, with every piece of steel made in penny numbers and hardened by empirical methods, and with lathes which any modern engineer would scorn, the construction of steam carriages, in which the parts had to be strong but as small and light as possible, was difficult enough without adding the complication of articulated levers, friction sheaves, variable-throw cranks, spring-loaded telescopic 'legs' and all the other contrivances needed very imperfectly to simulate animate motion. Nevertheless numerous 'walking engines' were designed, quite a number were made, and a few of them actually walked, after a fashion, to demonstrate that misplaced ingenuity can sometimes triumph over all obstacles.

The belief that it would not do to rely on the adhesion of a driving-wheel, or wheels, also influenced some of the railway pioneers and resulted, for example, in Blenkinsop's rack-and-pinion locomotive; but where the rail engineers soon appreciated that plain driving-wheels would suffice (at least for their gentle gradients), the fallacy continued to dominate some road-steamer designers until surprisingly late. It had its more useful offshoots in such things as Edge-worth's designs for a primitive track-laying vehicle, which he made as early as 1770, and the feet, or hinged plates, which Boydell attached to the driving wheels of his agricultural traction engines in the late 1840s. These were of some use on very soft ground though the inventor admitted that they wore badly and their upkeep was disastrously expensive.

Blenkinsop and other railway pioneers had the justification that they were faced with the problem of making locomotives which should have adhesion enough to draw heavy coal trains without being in themselves so heavy as to break the fragile colliery railroads of the time; otherwise the 'walking engine' could be dismissed as a mere eccentricity of no significance, if it did not illustrate a curious facet of the history of the mechanical vehicle. In most other branches of engineering the spread of knowledge and the appreciation of new discoveries were fairly rapid on the whole, but the history of the automobile affords more examples than any other branch of the art of improvements being invented, forgotten and re-invented, and of mistakes being similarly forgotten and their lessons being expensively re-learned. In his monumental work on the motor car, published in 1900, W. Worby Beaumont[5] remarked that all the designers working in the last twenty years of the nineteenth century had to learn again the lessons of the period 1820–40 'mostly by the process of making elaborate scrap'. This was certainly true of the exponents of the 'walking engine', and it seems very curious that they neither learned from one another's experience nor profited by Trevithick's demonstrations. W. Brunton, for example, was granted a patent for his 'mechanical traveller' in 1813 and after surmounting many difficulties succeeded in making an engine which, somewhat jerkily, hauled a loaded wagon at 2 m.p.h.; yet as a contributor to the *Mechanics' Magazine* it is hard to believe that Brunton was unacquainted with Trevithick's work.

More remarkable still were the efforts of David Gordon in a similar direction, for he was the father of Alexander Gordon whose book on *Elemental Locomotion* fully described all the known designs, whether actually made or merely drawn, for mechanical vehicles. In this book the author pays tribute to his father's help, yet this father was at one time as fervent as Brunton in his pursuit of the 'walking-engine' chimera. His first patent, of 1821, did not, it is

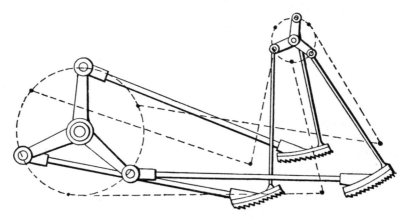

Figure 9 Gordon's arrangement of legs for his steam coaches

true, include the use of mechanical legs, but envisaged a carriage or wagon with steering-gear pushed from behind by a Trevithick-type road locomotive running not on its own wheels but mounted inside a huge drum nine feet in diameter and five feet wide. Two toothed rings were to be cut on the inside of this drum and the driving-wheels of the engine were to be correspondingly cogged to engage with them. Though this contrivance might have been efficacious as a road roller, it must have been very reluctant to negotiate sharp corners. It does not appear that this folly was ever put in hand, but between 1824 and 1830 Gordon constructed three or four* steam coaches in accordance with his patent of 1824. This provided for six mechanical feet, three either side, operated by a most ingenious system of cranks and connecting rods. The action was much less jerky than that of Brunton's bi-pedal creation, but after repeated trials Gordon found that wear and tear and breakdowns were excessive if he attempted anything more than a walking pace.

If it is odd that Gordon spent so much time and money before

* Nearly all the steam-carriage pioneers altered and rebuilt their machines so often that it is difficult to determine how many were made.

concluding, as he finally did, that the proper way to do the job was by applying power to the wheels, it is odder still that Goldsworthy Gurney also made his first steam carriages with mechanical legs, or propellers as he called them. For Gurney was a wealthy and well-educated man who, though not trained in engineering, had a wide knowledge of mechanical developments and was himself a Cornishman who ought surely to have known what his fellow Cornishman had done. Yet when he began his own steam carriage work in 1824–25 he was convinced, he wrote,[6] that:

> It was at this time a general opinion, and the fact was stated to me by eminent engineers, as 'settled by actual experiment', that if the power of any engine was applied to the wheels of a carriage on which it was mounted, with a view to propelling it along a common road, the wheels would turn round on the ground without moving the carriage forward. In explanation this effect was referred to the periphery of the wheel not having sufficient hold of the ground to make an available fulcrum. This came from such high authority, that I looked on it as a settled axiom in mechanics.

The year 1820 marks the start of intensive steam-carriage activity. During the ten years reign of George IV ideas abounded, companies were formed and the steam carriages which actually took the road came ever nearer to practicality. This activity continued even more briskly during the first years of William IV's brief reign, but by the time of his death the steam road coach had practically passed into limbo. The era thus neatly fits between the death of George III and the accession of Queen Victoria, and at the start of this period it has been estimated that there were over 5,000 steam engines at work in the mills and factories of Great Britain: by contrast there were only about 200 in France and fewer than 100 in Prussia. There was fierce opposition to the horseless vehicle, naturally enough, from all those thousands with vested interests in the horse-transport business, but the public imagination had been captured by the wonders of the steam age and looked fairly favourably on the idea of mechanical carriages. Much more favourably, indeed, than the later Victorians, who had grown resistant to innovation after nearly a century of prosperity and industrial superiority and were generally ready to share the Duke of Cambridge's view that 'all change, of whatever kind, or for whatever reason, is generally to be deprecated'.

It might seem that the steam-coach designers had plenty of experience to guide them, but the early nineteenth-century stationary and marine engines were very large, very heavy and very slow-moving; they drew steam at scarcely more than atmospheric pressure from vast beehive-shaped boilers of small efficiency. The steam-carriage men therefore had a host of new problems to solve. To pack the power needed into the space available (the automobile engineer's perennial difficulty) it was essential to work at high pressure by the standards of the time. This meant not only making high-pressure boilers which were light, small, strong and safe, but finding ways to make cylinders, pistons, pipes, glands, joints and the rest which would stand the pressure. Both materials and methods were sadly lacking in the necessary qualities, nevertheless the steam carriages were run at pressures between 70 p.s.i. and 250 p.s.i. at a time when 25 p.s.i. was still regarded as 'high pressure'. Boiler accidents were few, but other boiler deficiencies were manifest. Julius Griffith's steam coach of 1821, which was regarded as a triumph of engineering and was made for him by the celebrated Joseph Bramah, never took the road at all, because stationary tests in the factory yard discovered that the much-vaunted patent boiler primed so badly. At the other end of the scale Hancock's boilers appear to have been some seventy years ahead of their time and were most satisfactory.

Though the boilers and some ancilliary parts were often ahead of contemporary thought, some other aspects of steam-carriage design lagged behind. Having designed a light, compact boiler which could steam freely, and a suitable engine (generally twin-cylindered—a pair of engines in contemporary phrase) the designer had scarcely started on his problems. First came the question of transmission. Trevithick had used a countershaft and spur gears, but most of those who followed him preferred the simplicity of direct driving. This meant outside cylinders and crank-pins on the wheels or, more usually, a cranked live axle: this almost invariably meant an unsprung axle and was one of the most serious weaknesses. Forging a crankshaft presented problems enough to late-Georgian technology, but when to the torsional stresses from the crank throws was added the strain of acting as axle tree carrying a heavy load, unsprung, over rough surfaces it can be seen why crank-axle failures were common. Rather more honestly than some of his contemporaries, Colonel Maceroni recorded four crank-axle failures and wrote:[7]

Cranked axles, of four to five inches diameter, are so difficult to make in a common forge, with sledge hammers, that not one in five, so made, by the best firemen, will prove perfectly sound. I have now had them made under a tilt hammer, weighing three tons, which turns them out as sound as wax. It was in direct opposition to my will and remonstrances that Mr Squire (who had been placed in possession of the premises) persisted in attempting to make the axles at our own common forge. The consequence of the four interruptions occasioned by these breakings of our axle trees, have been more distressing and injurious and paralysing to me than I have space to describe.

A few road coaches were made (notably by Scott Russell) with spur-gear transmission from a countershaft arranged with some form of radius link which allowed the axle to be spring mounted and yet to maintain the correct 'pitching' of driving and driven gear wheels. This meant restricting the spring action, but was, of course, a great improvement on the unsprung axle. Hancock and James used chain transmission which will be described later.

The need to allow differential action of the driving-wheels on curves was at once apparent and was usually met by the simple but crude expedient of driving normally on one wheel only, leaving the other free to revolve round the axle shaft but with some form of claw clutch or bolt so that it could be 'clutched in' to give extra adhesion on hills or soft roads. This system meant either that the engineer neglected to declutch and imposed extra strain on the axle by running with both wheels fixed, or that one hind wheel took an unfair share of the work.

Ratchet clutches and other devices were also tried, but the 'modern' form of differential gear was not, curiously enough, used in England except on one experimental vehicle made by Sharp, Roberts and Co. of Manchester in 1833. This made only one or two short trips, as it was one of the few steam coaches to suffer a burst boiler, which caused it to be laid aside. F. Hill, whose road steamer of 1840 was one of the most successful, sketched designs for a differential axle (acknowledging his debt to Richard Roberts for the idea), but did not use it himself. * Yet the common differential gear was

* William Fletcher (*Steam Locomotion on Common Roads*) states that Hill's 1840 coach was fitted with differential gear. Other authorities say it was not and the conjectural drawings appear to support the majority.

known long before the steam-carriage era; in a slightly different form it had been used as a multiplying gear for rotary fire blowers and it had been used occasionally in elaborate astronomical clocks since the sixteenth century. Its ancestry can, indeed, be traced to pre-Christian times and George Lanchester (younger brother of Dr Frederick Lanchester, whom he helped to build Britain's first four-wheeled petrol car) has proved beyond reasonable doubt that the essential element of the 'Yellow Emperor's South-pointing Chariot' was a differential gear.[8]

In their arrangements for steering the steam-coach men showed a similarly conservative approach, all but one using the conventional horsed-vehicle type of centre-pivoted forecarriage and devoting their ingenuity to devising means of controlling it. The 'pilot-wheel' system favoured by Gurney on his large coach looked cumbersome, but gave good results as it restored the leverage normally provided by the horses and shafts, and was less likely than other systems to be jerked out of control if one wheel struck an obstacle. Several designers used a chain and sprocket reduction gear for steering, and Hancock added the refinement of a pedal-controlled damper to relieve the steersman's wrists of strain. James designed a particularly ingenious quick-thread arrangement, but only the abortive Griffiths coach of 1821 appears to have had radial-axle or Ackermann steering. As noted in Chapter 6, this much superior system had been patented in England in 1818, but it was certainly devised at least a hundred years earlier. An arrangement rather similar to the Lenkensperger/ Ackermann had been sketched by Edgeworth in 1775 and he, in his turn, acknowledged that a sailing-carriage depicted in the third volume of *Machines approuvées par l'Academie Royal des Sciences*, published in 1714, was steered on the Ackermann principle.

Water consumption, on average, was about ten gallons a mile, which posed another problem. Hancock, Gurney, Maceroni and all who wrote on the matter pointed out that once regular services were established relay stations would be set up, with piped water supplies and hosepipes, whereupon this nuisance would be abolished. But as only two or three very short-lived, short-stage, commercial services were established, the relay stations were never set up, and the business of filling tanks with a hundred gallons or more, from stable pump or horse trough with buckets, often took twenty minutes or more. During this time the fire would slacken, so when the vehicle moved off its performance would be sluggish for a mile or so. In order to avoid noise the Trevithick-type exhaust blast was not much used (Gurney, indeed, claimed it as a new invention in 1828) and most road steamers had mechanical bellows or fans driven from the engine: and as these stopped when the carriage stopped so the fire slackened for lack of draught. On some of his later vehicles Hancock appears to have arranged a dog-clutch connection to allow the engine, and consequently the blower and water pump, to keep going whilst the carriage stood; on his big coach Gurney solved the problem neatly by providing a little donkey engine, in the fore boot, which drove the fan and water pump independently of the main engine. The obvious solution of using a condenser usually posed more problems than it solved, though it was often tried. An air-cooled condenser small enough for the available space was not efficient enough to create a vacuum, and thereby assist the engine as the water-cooled condenser of a stationary or marine installation does, but tended to hinder it by creating back pressure. Also, the tallow used as a lubricant was carried over with the exhaust and reduced the efficiency of the condenser by coating the tubes; or, worse, still, lubricant in suspension would get back to the boiler and cause violent foaming and priming.

In order to avoid making smoke which would inevitably have aroused opposition, coke was burnt, and this also presented difficulties as it was more difficult to keep a clean fire with coke than with coal in the small furnace of a steam carriage. Since gas-lighting had come into use it was a fuel fairly easily come by in, or near, large towns, but by no means generally available as the steam-coach men found to their cost when they essayed long journeys. When Hancock drove one of his machines from London to Brighton and back in November 1832 he was held up for a long while on the outward journey whilst coke was fetched from Croydon by horse and cart, and on the return journey it was found difficult to maintain a head of steam, as the coke from the Hove gas-works was of lower calorific value than the London stuff. This was attributed to the greater efficiency of Hove's fire-clay retorts, which yielded 12,000 cubic feet of gas per chaldron of coal against the 10,000 feet produced by London's iron retorts.

With hindsight it is easy to see the mistakes made by the designers and promoters of these steam vehicles, and a fundamental one, undoubtedly, was their attempt to compete with the stage-coaches. It is true that some of them talked of using steam for goods haulage (and if regular steam carrier services had been established many of the hopelessly uneconomic branch railways need never have been built), but the sheer glamour and popularity of the horse coaches naturally tempted the steam enthusiasts to try to vie with them. This not only brought powerful vested interests against them, but led to many of the steamers being made for speeds too great for the materials and roads of the time.

The idea unfortunately got about that steam was not well suited to slow, heavy work, and this was reinforced by Sir Goldsworthy Gurney in his evidence to the Select Committee of the House of Commons when he said that his experience proved the advantages of steam were proportionately greater as the speed increased. To this truth he added the rider that horse traction was cheaper than steam traction at speeds below five or six miles an hour. This was a clear case of arguing from the particular to the general which has so often bedevilled legislation affecting technical matters. With his particular arrangement of engines, of two-cylinders, nine inches bore and eighteen inches stroke, at a working pressure between 70 and 100 p.s.i. with no variable cut-off, Gurney found that a piston speed of 220 feet per minute gave the best fuel economy; with cranks formed directly on the hind axle and with driving-wheels five feet in diameter this piston speed corresponded with something just over ten miles an hour, but the possibility of attaining equal fuel economy at a slower speed by the use of reducing-gear or smaller wheels was not put before the committee.

In most histories of automobile engineering it is implied that it was the stupidity of the legislature alone which put a stop to steam-coach development. This is less than just, as Parliament was not so much unreasonable as unwilling to breach the honoured principle of interfering as little as possible with established local authorities. The real opposition came from highway authorities and turnpike trusts. The former naturally, but short-sightedly, objected because of the weight of the road steamers. To this the steam advocates replied that with no horses' hoofs to pound the road and with tyres between four and five inches wide the steam coach damaged the road less than a four-horse coach running on two-and-a-half-inch tyres. There was some truth in this, but reading between the lines it is clear that the steamers were rather heavier than their advocates made out, and on the soft roads of the time the authorities were justifiably apprehensive that juggernauts of three to five tons, running at speeds up to 20 m.p.h., would soon cause trouble.

The trustees shared this fear, but were far more concerned about the potential threat to the horse's monopoly of road transport. Although there may not have been many actual coach proprietors on the trusts their influence we felt in many ways, and nearly all the landowners, farmers and others who sat on the trusts were financially interested in one way or another in the huge industry which was supported on the horse's back. From about 1825 onwards, as Turnpike Acts fell due for renewal, different trusts were given power to impose prohibitory tolls on steam vehicles. In his evidence before the 1831 committee, Gurney cited the following authorizations:

Liverpool to Prescot road	4-horse coach 4s.	steamer £2–8–0
Bathgate road	4-horse coach 5s.	steamer £1–7–1
Ashburnham to Totnes road	4-horse coach 3s.	steamer £2–0–0

The committee was set up as a result of Gurney's petition; he claimed to have spent £30,000 in five years, under the supposed protection of the patent laws, and he now saw his work and expenditure being nullified by Parliament's action in permitting such impositions.

The committee was wholly in favour of mechanical traction, and recommended removing the punitive tolls and taking various other steps to encourage development. Some of the evidence of the steam-coach advocates may have been biased, and one can detect examples of *suppressio veri, suggestio falsi* in some of Gurney's statements, but nothing could gainsay the fact that there were at least a million horses employed in road transport, quite apart from those solely used for agriculture or sport, and as it was common ground that one horse consumed as much as eight men the needs of a rapidly growing population could only be met by reducing this drain on resources. The report concluded: 'These enquiries have led the House of Commons to believe that the substitution of inanimate for animate power in draught on common roads is one of the most important improvements in the means of inland communication ever produced.'

Alas, the gap between that which a Select Committee recommends and that which appears on the statue book yawns wide, and the only practical outcome of the recommendations was that mechanically propelled hackney carriages were exempted from carriage duty. A very progressive Steam Carriage Bill passed the Commons and was narrowly defeated on technicalities in the Lords; the Government intended to modify it enough to meet the objections and to re-introduce it, but all such minor legislation was swamped in the maelstrom of the Reform Bill in 1832. After that it was too late to save the day; with the success of the Liverpool and Manchester Railways, and with so many other lines being hurriedly planned, the best engineering talents joined the financial world in preparing for the railway boom.

Steam was not the only proposed 'substitute for animate power'. In 1826 Samuel Brown designed a most ingenious carriage driven by a modified form of his patent gas-vacuum engine, and demonstrated its ability to climb Shooters Hill. A company was formed to exploit the invention (primarily for use in canal boats), but it was soon clear that the Brown engine lagged far behind the steam engine for efficiency and fuel economy. When it is learnt that the two-cylinder carriage engine developed only four horsepower despite its twelve-inch bore and twenty-four-inch stroke, one can see why this ancestor of the internal-combustion car remained an isolated experiment.

On a less serious level were the many hopeful inventors who designed carriages propelled by muscle-power. In most of these some luckless lackey had to strain at the treadles or levers, but all three occupants of the Trivector were expected to work their passage. Even with this improvement to the power-weight ratio the burden, at seven hundredweight, was still considerable, and the three stalwarts who made a Trivector trip from London to Brighton in the autumn of 1819 took nearly twelve hours. Doubtless they would have agreed with the principal guest at some village function in Ireland who was conveyed in a decayed sedan chair which had neither seat nor bottom: had it not been for the honour of the thing, he opined, he would sooner have walked.

CHAPTER ELEVEN

Steam: The Second Phase

The first serious attempts to mechanize road transport were frustrated by joint forces to which Parliament contributed only indirectly, and apart from some isolated and insignificant experiments it was more than twenty years before the second phase started. To appreciate this second phase it is essential to take a closer look at those of the first period who came nearest to commercial success; not only to see what had been learnt by 1840 but what had been forgotten by 1880.

In many nineteenth-century accounts (and some of later date) Goldsworthy Gurney is hailed as the man who brought the steam-coach dream nearest to reality. This was certainly so in his own estimation. Because he was a fairly prominent and pushing figure, destined at birth, it seems, for the knighthood bestowed on him in middle life; because he had a good conceit of himself and the ability to ignore awkward truths; because it was largely on his account that the Parliamentary Committee of 1831 was set up; because he was of a social order which entitled him to a distant 'How d'ye do?' from the Duke of Wellington (who once rode behind one of his steam 'drags'), and because his later inventions, such as the Gurney stove and the Bude light, earned him a lot of money and kept his name before the public, it is easy to see why he was given first place; but not all his contemporaries agreed with this verdict.

Colonel Maceroni was associated with Gurney's early attempts and felt that he was dishonestly treated over the business. It is true that Maceroni always blamed his many misfortunes on the dishonesty and stupidity of others until he seems almost to be bordering upon mania, and one of his milder passages reads: 'There is in particular one sculking anonymous slanderer, who signs himself H[ancock]. By reference to No. 603 of the *Mechanics Magazine* it will be seen that I

175

called upon the insolent poltroon to show his face; but he has not done so.' Nevertheless, his opinions of Gurney's mechanical ability are worth quoting.

'In 1829', he wrote, 'having long been thoroughly convinced of the incapacity of Mr Gurney's boiler and machinery, I abandoned all further thoughts of the business and went to Constantinople to serve the Mussulmans against the Russians.' He later refers to the help he gave Gurney in raising funds to the tune of £20,000 and Gurney's failure to honour his agreements; then follows this passage: 'Had I been stupid enough to copy any of his miserable pretended mechanical "arrangements", or his still more miserable and utterly useless boiler . . . the legal course was open to him.' On his return to England in 1831 Maceroni was approached for help and advice by John Squire, who had built a steam carriage which Maceroni describes as: ' . . . much superior to anything that had been constructed by Mr Gurney, but still it had a *tubular* [i.e. a water-tube] boiler, and occasionally threw the water out along with the steam, as always occurred to Gurney's boilers, whether with or without the "separators" as he had variously constructed them.'

As the financial hopes of nearly all the steam carriage designers rested on the possibility of selling manufacturing or patent rights, and as the only patentable features of steam vehicles were the 'arrangements of machinery' (which were difficult to define or protect) and special components, such as boilers, it will be seen that boiler design was of paramount importance.

As we have seen, Gurney was convinced, at first, that mechanical legs were necessary and his first vehicle relied entirely on this mode of propulsion; it worked, after a fashion, but the 'propellers' were very troublesome as Gurney admitted. Of his second attempt (probably a rebuild of the first) he wrote: '. . . after numerous experiments to get rid of the difficulty [with the legs] we united the wheels to the propellers, and so constructed them that should the wheel slip . . . the propellers could be brought into action'. It needed only a few trial trips to prove that it never was necessary to use the propellers, and on all his subsequent machines Gurney relied on ordinary driving-wheels.

Although it was modified in detail many times, Gurney's boiler remained fundamentally unaltered during the eight years of his steam-carriage work. Making due allowance for his exaggeration, it does seem to have justified Maceroni's jibes to the extent that it was never quite cured of priming; otherwise it was by no means as bad as he made out. It consisted of two horizontal drums or trunks, placed one above the other some two to three feet apart, connected by vertical water standards which formed supporting pillars for the upper trunk. Top and bottom trunks were also connected by a series of tubes roughly in the form of a capital U laid on its side, so that the lower arms of these U-pipes formed the bars of the grate. The steam was drawn from the upper trunk and passed into two (or more) vertical receivers which served as separators; these separators contained water in their lower portions and were connected to the bottom trunk of the boiler itself. The steam pipes from the tops of the separators communicated with a main feed pipe which passed over the fire on its way to the control valve and engine, and thus the steam was dried and partly superheated.

One of the modifications which Sir Charles Dance made to Gurney's boiler was to make the boiler tubes in three pieces, united by cast-iron screwed elbows, instead of bending them in one piece. This made a stronger job, and allowed the insertion of cleaning plugs in the elbows, but a good deal of trouble was still experienced with bursting tubes. The boiler was quite safe, and passengers were often unaware (until the coach stopped) that a tube had burst; but there was considerable public suspicion of high-pressure boilers, and the youthful Charles Dickens[1], wrote in 1843 that travelling in a Mississippi steamboat, with its constant 'high-pressure snorting', was comparable to living on the first floor of a powder mill and leaning over the landing balusters with a lighted candle.

Gurney's boilers were tested to 200 p.s.i. cold and were normally worked at between 70 and 120 p.s.i., evaporating about five pounds of water for each pound of coke.

Gurney described his large fourteen-seater coach (Plate 25) of 1828 as perfect, but it seems to have been far from successful, and one suspects that the cranked driving-axle suffered from the lack of rigidity of the long 'chassis' which consisted of the old-fashioned timber perch supplemented by a pair of longitudinal sills. It was, nevertheless, a remarkably well-planned vehicle by the standards of the time. As already stated, the feed-water pumps and fire blower were driven by a donkey engine below the fore boot, and exhaust steam from this and the main engines was silenced by passing through the flat feed-water tank, thus heating it, which hung below the perch, before being ejected into the flue.

The coach weighed about three and a half tons unladen and at 40 p.s.i. in the steam-chest the output from the two-cylinder (9 inches by 18 inches) engine was about 28 h.p. There were no brakes, but the steam control cock and the reversing lever were under the steersman's control. There was no variable cut-off and the slide valves were worked by eccentrics, rods and rocking links; the motion was reversed by raising the eccentric rods from bottom to top of the slotted links by cables connected to the reversing lever and guided by suitable pulleys. This could only be done when the vehicle was stationary, and Gurney's statement to the Parliamentary Committee that hills could be descended in perfect safety, as the engines could be reversed, was only true if the machine was stopped at the brow of the hill, the rods lifted to reverse position and the coach then allowed to roll forward by gravity with the steam available to retard it if it began to run too fast.

It is not quite clear how many '1828 models' with the auxiliary engines were made, but there were probably two, though one of them may have been a rebuild of the 1826–27 experiment. Many works illustrate a whole view and a cutaway view which is allegedly of the same vehicle, but which on close examination, is seen to represent two outwardly similar coaches with different forms of pilot-wheel steering, steam separators, smoke stack, and other details.

It was with the 1828 pattern of coach that Gurney made his not-very-successful Bath excursion which is so often wrongly represented as part of a regular 15 m.p.h. service, and it was presumably because of this experience that all his subsequent machines were of the steam 'drag' or light, high-speed tractor variety designed to tow a passenger or goods vehicle behind them.

In view of the weights involved, and the public fear of boiler explosions, the steam drag idea was a sensible one; but the logical step of removing the front wheels from the towed vehicle and mounting its forecarriage on a suitable pivot at the back of the drag, so as to form a compact six-wheeled articulated vehicle, was not taken until some seventy years later, when De Dion Bouton et Trépardoux made a number of steam carriages on this plan.

To save space on the 1829 pattern drags the auxiliary engine was done away with and exhaust blast was used to urge the furnace. The boiler was modified with a single horizontal separator in place of the vertical ones. The engine mounted on the perch, the valve motion and the cranked driving-axle were much as before, but both wheels were free to revolve round the axle and were driven by T-arms,

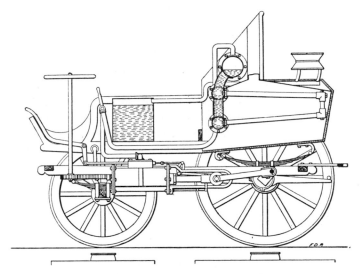

Figure 10 Gurney's 1829 pattern 'drag'

fixed to the shaft, which bore on removable pins or bolts in the wheel felloes. Normally only one wheel was driven and the bolts were put in the second one only when extra adhesion was needed; but even with all the bolts in place the crank axle was relieved of some torsional stress, as each wheel could make a half turn of free movement. By putting the driving-pins in the felloes the spokes were relieved of driving strain, and this feature of Gurney's drag was also revived by De Dion Bouton et Trépardoux.

Six or seven of Gurney's drags were constructed; they were much more reliable than his more impressive-looking coach and came very near to commercial success. A company was formed in Glasgow to operate a steam service with them between that city and Edinburgh, but this venture failed. According to Gurney this was because the failure of the Cheltenham–Gloucester service discouraged the would-be investors, but according to Maceroni the speculators, though at first ready to pay £45,000 for the patent rights, cried off when the demonstration drag, sent by sea to Leith, took three days to cover the forty-two miles between the cities and finished the journey igno-miniously horse-drawn.

A Welsh venture is also mentioned, and one motor historian[2] has added to Gurney-mythology by saying that for this purpose one of the coaches with the mechanical legs was driven to Wales, served on the Holyhead road and finally met a humiliating end by being con-verted into a tramcar. This is how history is made. The vehicle in question was one of the 1829-pattern drags, not a coach, which was horse-drawn, not driven, to Hirewan, where its road wheels were removed and flanged wheels substituted, so that it could be put to work, as planned, drawing coal wagons on a colliery tramroad.

On 21 February 1831 Sir Charles Dance started a four-trips-a-day service between Cheltenham and Gloucester with Gurney drags fitted with his modified form of boiler. This service ran regularly and without accident, Sundays excepted, until 22 June and passengers were carried in omnibus trailers with seats for sixteen. The total distance covered was 3,640 miles and some 4,000 paying passengers were carried in addition to an uncounted number who were given free rides. The average running time for the nine miles was fifty minutes, but on more than one occasion this was cut to forty minutes, and on the day of the Gloucester election thirty-eight paying passengers were carried on one trip.

The fares were only half those charged on the stage-coach and the expenditure on coke for the service (for many extra-schedule and trial runs were made) amounted to 9s. a day against the estimated 45s. a day for eighteen horses needed for a comparable horsed service. Allowing for capital cost and standing charges this looks promising, but it is fairly certain that Gurney and Dance minimized the repair costs. In his pamphlet Gurney makes the project look more successful than it was by implying that all the work was done by one drag; but, in fact, three were supplied, so that two could be kept in work whilst the third was under repair. Gurney reprints the table, prepared for the Parliamentary Committee, which shows each day's running times, passengers carried and other details, and this has occasional footnotes to explain exceptionally slow journeys. These notes refer only to trivial causes such as 'new stoker' or 'pump valve unseated', yet we know from Dance's letters that there were also delays from burst boiler tubes and other breakdowns.

The brave attempt was finally ended when large stones were strewn across the road to a depth of eighteen inches by order, so Gurney alleges, of the turnpike trustees. After struggling through these obstructions three times the crank axle broke between the throws, and this mishap coincided with the renewal of the Cheltenham Road Bill with a clause which authorized a heavy toll on steam carriages.

It may well be that Dance was not displeased to have these good excuses for withdrawing the service, and it is significant that soon after the venture had collapsed he took one of his Gurney drags to Maudslay Sons and Field of Lambeth to be reboilered yet again. This resulted in a new patent in the joint names of Field and Dance for an improved boiler which, in its turn, was developed into the well-known Field boiler, with hanging tubes, which powered so many Victorian fire-engines, river launches and other devices

All Gurney's contemporaries appear to have shared with him (as did the rail engineers of the time) the use of a fixed cut-off, with control entirely by throttling or 'wire-drawing'. Also, most of the steam coaches seem to have had small steam pipes in relation to cylinder and valve port areas. Steam-chest pressures were consequently about 15–25 per cent below boiler pressures. This rather inefficient arrangement was probably adopted to lessen the risk of priming, but gave the fortuitous advantage of great engine flexibility which suited the single-ratio transmission usually adopted. It is significant that the most successful of the Edwardian steam cars, the Stanley, which also had fixed-ratio transmission, had small throttle apertures and steam pipes so that steam-chest pressure was little more than half of boiler pressure: yet the Stanleys were particularly noted for their flexibility and acceleration.

The Glasgow to Paisley service operated by the Steam Carriage Company of Scotland for seven months of 1834 suffered a fate similar to Dance's Gloucestershire experiment. This Company worked six 26-seater steam coaches made by the Grove House Engine Works of Edinburgh to the designs of John Scott Russell. In one important respect these machines were superior to Gurney's, as the back axles were hung on semi-elliptic springs, and the motion from the vertical two-cylinder (12 inches by 12 inches) engines was conveyed by crossheads and external connecting-rods to two crankshafts, one to each cylinder, and thence by two-to-one spur gearing to the live axle, which was guided by ingenious linkwork so that the correct pitching of the gears was not affected by the axle rising and falling on the springs. The Company also adopted the excellent plan of carrying enough fuel and water for each stage in a two-wheeled trailer, which also provided comfortable seating for six more travellers. At the end of each journey it was the work of a moment to disconnect an empty tender and hitch on a loaded one, so it was easy to maintain a running time of forty minutes for the seven-mile journey, allowing for half a dozen intermediate stops, and with a coach leaving each terminal point regularly on the hour. As many as forty-five passengers at a time were often carried, and the steamers were popular.

In other respects Russell's design was less felicitous than Gurney's; each coach needed a crew of three—steersman, stoker and engine-man, and the steersman had to rely on the engineman, seated right at the back of the coach, to control the engine. The boiler seems to have been similar, but inferior, to Hancock's, with a large number of flat, thin-walled vertical water chambers separated and supported by iron stay rods. According to Fletcher, the walls of the chambers were of one-tenth inch copper and 1,300 quarter-inch stays were needed to support them.

Russell made the usual claims about the safety of his boiler, and said that the failure of a stay, or excess pressure, would only result in leakage from one chamber at a time, and that the escape of steam would be too small to be dangerous; but when one of the carriages was struggling through a heap of loose stones, deliberately placed across the road by order of the trustees to obstruct the steam vehicles, a wheel collapsed, the boiler burst and five people were killed. This was, presumably, the first fatal motor accident in Great Britain.

The Court of Session interdicted the whole fleet of steam carriages from running, and the Company brought an action for damages against the turnpike trustees which was finally settled out of court. The damage had been done, however; the service was never re-started, four of the coaches were dismantled by the makers and the remaining two were sent to London, where they were offered for sale. They made daily demonstration runs, for some weeks, from Hyde Park Corner to Hammersmith and back, but there were no takers and they, too, were broken up.

25 Scale model of Gurney's 1828 steam coach

26 W. H. James's remarkably advanced design of 1832 for a steam 'drag'

If sheer perseverance was the only criterion, the steam-carriage prize should go to Walter Hancock, who also qualifies on several other counts; notably for his patent boiler which gave admirable results and appears to have been perfectly safe. It is true that a stoker was killed by a boiler explosion on one of Hancock's omnibuses (the *Enterprise*), but the coroner's jury accepted the evidence that he had fastened the safety valve down whilst running the engine and blower, disconnected from the transmission, on a small admission of steam to urge the fire. *

In 1824 Hancock, then twenty-five years old, patented and made a novel form of steam engine which had rubber bags in place of conventional cylinders and pistons; the inflation and deflation of the bags gave motion to connecting-rods and cranks. This cheap and simple engine worked well, at low pressures, and as it is unlikely that untreated natural rubber could have stood the temperature it must be assumed that Hancock had evolved some means of 'vulcanizing' fifteen years before Charles Goodyear patented his process in America. A four h.p. engine on this plan drove the machinery in Hancock's workshop at Stratford for some years, and early in 1825 he decided to use one to drive a steam carriage. Presumably because it was unsuited to high-pressure working, and was therefore too bulky, the rubber-bag machine did not made a satisfactory automobile engine, but the experiment sufficed to turn the inventor's thoughts to steam road locomotion by more conventional means.

The next attempt took the form of a four-seater, three-wheeled carriage with the single front wheel, Cugnot-fashion, acting both as driver and steerer, being rotated by a pair of oscillating cylinders one either side of the forks. The necessary flexible steam connections were troublesome and the water-tube boiler did not come up to expectations, so the engine was removed, the rest scrapped and a new carriage constructed.

This was the *Infant*, which had ten seats, four wheels and the oscillating engine carried on an outrigger frame behind the back axle, which it drove by chain. This meant that the axle could be

---

* This evidence may not be wholly reliable, as the chief witness was no more, and it seems odd that an experienced man (as he was said to be) did not realize that tying down the safety valve would not hasten the generation of steam below the point at which the valve would normally lift.

hung on springs, but the most important feature was the new boiler, for which a patent was granted in 1827.

This boiler consisted of a series of narrow, parallel water chambers arranged vertically, rather similar in appearance to modern domestic

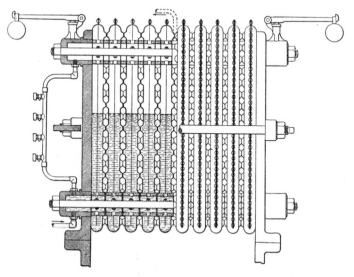

Figure 11 Hancock's boiler for steam carriages

heating radiators, with criss-crossed iron stays horizontally and vertically disposed between them. In the course of experiments Hancock found that the thin walls of the water chambers tended to bulge over the stays, and he took advantage of this by making the walls thinner still and encouraging them to bulge, by raising the pressure far above normal, until the bulging portions of adjacent chambers touched, thereby giving and receiving support and increasing the surface area in contact with the hot gases. The next step was to emboss the plates before assembly and so to do away with most of the stays, with a further increase in heating area.

The furnace arrangements were ingenious and ultimately included hopper-feed for the coke, and a rack and pinion device which allowed clinkered fire-bars to be removed, drawing in a fresh set behind them, without dropping the fire. On his last three vehicles Hancock arranged the furnace slightly to one side, instead of directly below, the water chambers and passed part of the exhaust steam over the fire to generate water-gas and aid combustion.

In its final form the efficiency of Hancock's boiler was double that of the Gurney, and the figures available for his *Automaton* show that the heating surface was about 85 sq. feet, which, with a grate surface of 6 sq. feet, evaporated ten pounds of water for each pound of coke burnt. Working through a two-cylinder (9 inches by 12 inches) engine developing about 24 h.p. for 70 p.s.i. boiler pressure, and making 70 revolutions a minute at ten miles an hour, the boiler output of the *Automaton* was one effective horsepower for 5 sq. feet of heating surface and 0.3 sq. feet of grate area.[3] These figures would have been commendable for 1900 and were remarkable for 1830.

The *Infant* was soon rebuilt so completely as to be virtually a new-born infant. The body was enlarged into a fourteen-seater *char-à-banc*, and the oscillating engine was removed from its exposed and dirty position and replaced by a fixed-cylinder vertical engine enclosed in a compartment, with room for an engineman beside it, just ahead of the boiler. The single-chain transmission remained as before, with the addition of screwed radius arms to maintain the correct chain tension. As this was an ordinary link chain, passing over grooved and spiked pulleys, it must have been rough and noisy by modern standards, but it was well protected by an undershield. As the engine parts were also enclosed, Hancock may claim to have been the first automobile engineer to recognize that lubrication by mud and optimism seldom gives good results.

Although Hancock's subsequent vehicles were given many detail improvements, and were fitted with various styles of bodywork, they followed the rebuilt *Infant* in general plan. Like the Scott Russell coaches, they carried a crew of three, but on all of them the engine was under the control of the steersman. On his last three carriages Hancock fitted shoe brakes acting on the hind wheels, but it was part of the stokers' duty to work these.

The rebuilt *Infant* ran to Brighton and back, encountered difficulty with fuel supplies, as we have seen, and suffered a breakdown also, as one of the flanges of Hancock's patent wheels (described in Chapter 5) cracked as a result of having been cast too thinly. On another Brighton trip the dog-clutch which put the blower in or out of action jammed and the cast-iron gear wheel driving the fan broke;

but all things considered there were commendably few teething troubles with Hancock's machines. On one occasion, he records in his Narrative that when the *Infant* was working at 100 p.s.i. pressure four of the boiler chambers split without any of the thirteen passengers being aware of it. The London and Brighton Steam Carriage Company which was launched in 1832 came to nothing, and these demonstration runs were consequently wasted; but the *Infant* was often run for hire between Stratford and London.

The London and Paddington Steam Carriage Company behaved particularly shabbily to Hancock. He built his fourteen-seater omnibus, the *Enterprise*, for them on the understanding that if the trials satisfied the Directors they would buy two more similar buses. Under Hancock's personal guidance, the *Enterprise* ran a twice- or thrice-daily service between Paddington and the Bank for sixteen successive days. It was filled to overflowing on each trip, was piloted through the busy streets without difficulty and often made 16 m.p.h. The Company's engineer reported favourably, the Directors expressed satisfaction, the *Enterprise* was handed over and Hancock spent most of the next four months in abortive negotiations and letter-writing trying to make the Company fulfil their obligations. During this time their engineer, D. Redmund, dismantled the *Enterprise*, copied all the essential parts, and assembled a carriage of his own which apparently differed from Hancock's only in having a different steering-gear and some elaborately useless spring wheels. Redmund's inferior copy of Hancock's boiler was a very poor article, the vehicle never steamed properly, the Company failed and although Hancock re-possessed the *Enterprise* he lost nearly £1,000 over the transaction.

A rather similar fate befell the *Era*, an eighteen-seat vehicle designed for a Greenwich company which came to nothing. In due time the *Era* was rebodied, renamed *Erin* and sent to Dublin, where there was considerable interest in steam-coach operations, mostly centred upon the activities of Sir James Anderson, the 'Steam-Knight of Buttevant Castle'. After eight expensive weeks of demonstrations and negotiations, it was clear that nothing would come of the venture and the *Erin* returned to England.

Hopes of a commercial deal revived again when an Austrian firm ordered a steam bus for use in Vienna, with hints of more orders to follow. The vehicle was built in the remarkable time of six weeks, but just before completion the buyers asked Hancock to shorten it and convert it into a six-seat 'drag' to tow ordinary carriages or coaches. They then refused to pay for the alterations and finally cancelled the deal altogether. The machine was altered yet again and finally took the road as a twenty-two-seat* *char-à-banc*, similar in most mechanical details to the slightly smaller *Autopsy* which had been intended for the Brighton work. In its final form it was named '*Automaton*'.

Apart from his own steam phaeton, of which he was very proud, Hancock considered the *Automaton*, with good reason, as the best of all his carriages. It was also the most powerful, with engines of twelve inches bore; it seems to have been very reliable by the standards of the time and was quite often timed at well over 20 m.p.h. fully loaded. Its last recorded run was made in July 1840 when it was hired by the Stratford Cricket Club to take the team and twenty-one supporters to a match at Epping, where, incidentally, the steamer attracted far more attention than the game. With its thirty-two passengers and crew of three aboard, the *Automaton* must have weighed some four tons, but it is believed to have touched 25 m.p.h. on the return journey.

Apart from the Paddington to the Bank service worked by the *Enterprise*, other Hancock vehicles ran regular services in and around London at different times. The *Autopsy* worked between Finsbury and Pentonville for some weeks and then, in company with the *Era*, was run from Moorgate to Paddington and back via the Bank; some 4,000 passengers were carried on this service.

In 1835, after its Dublin foray, the *Erin* made demonstration trips to Marlborough, to Reading and to Birmingham. A London to Birmingham Steam Coach Company was formed, the usual grandiose plans were made and it was announced that the fares would be £1 inside and 10s. outside; but in the face of more toll increases and with railway talk growing louder this company joined the others in oblivion—as did another formed to exploit Dr Church's improbable-looking steam coach over the same route.

In May 1836 Hancock started his most ambitious attempt to prove that steam road transport should be taken seriously. The *Autopsy*, the *Automaton* and the *Erin* (now, according to one contemporary print again called *Era*), with stand-by help from the old *Infant*, worked various routes for nearly five months with fair regularity.

* Eighteen seats inside, four outside.

Five hundred and twenty-five trips were made from the City to Islington and back, 143 to Paddington and back and 44 to Stratford and back. The city was traversed more than 200 times: despite some provocative and foolhardy attempts by stage-coach drivers and other horsemen to hamper the steamers, there were no accidents and 12,761 passengers were carried. These impressive demonstrations did nothing to halt the increases in tolls, nor did the speculations and proposals for new steam-carriage companies materialize. It is very noticeable how much capital was raised in support of steam-carriage designers who never made a vehicle which ran satisfactorily, and how little was forthcoming for the really worthy designs of men like James, Hancock or Maceroni.

If Hancock's experience of the financial and company-promoting gentry was disappointing, Maceroni's was disastrous. It may well be that this bombastic, ingenious, Anglo-Italian soldier-inventor was given to exaggeration (Maceroni's 'never-failing fountain of vapour' was how one contemporary described his assertions), and it might seem that he learned his vituperative literary style from the celebrated editor of the *Eatanswill Gazette*, but there is no doubt that he suffered much from the chicanery of financial sharks. Over one transaction in particular he had the mortification of seeing others grow rich whilst he remained poor. This was when lack of means prevented him from taking his two carriages to the Continent to demonstrate to interested parties in Belgium and France; he was obliged to hand the negotiation over to an Italian Jew named Asda, who undertook to return the vehicles within six weeks and to pay Maceroni £1,500 for the patent rights.

Asda demonstrated the carriages in Brussels and Paris to such good effect that he received £16,000 for manufacturing rights of which 'poor Maceroni never received a shilling', as Fletcher put it.[4] As a result of this débâcle all the tools and machinery at Maceroni's Paddington workshop were seized by his creditors, and his chances of raising capital elsewhere still further reduced in consequence. Nevertheless, he tried again and again; success seemed to be within his reach at last when, as late as 1841, the General Steam Carriage Company was launched to operate steamers built to Maceroni's design. As he was in no position to have them constructed on his premises, the contract went to Beale's factory at East Greenwich, and things seemd to be shaping well when the directors and principal shareholders were given a trial run on the first Beale-built Maceroni. No difficulty was found in traversing crowded South London streets at 16 m.p.h., and with seventeen aboard the dreaded Shooter's Hill was climbed at 8 m.p.h. Then came the blow; having contracted to supply the carriages at £800 apiece, Beale now demanded £1,100 and refused to hand over the completed one for less. Though not directly concerned in the quarrel, Maceroni was the sufferer, as, once again, the transaction collapsed.

Maceroni's last word on the steam-carriage topic was in a letter to the *Mechanic's Magazine* in 1843 pointing out that Squire's newly granted patent for a boiler was an infringement of the original Maceroni and Squire patent of 1833. Whether this was so or not, it is evident, from the spectacular performances so often recorded by unbiased observers of the Maceroni carriages, that the boiler was extremely efficient. In view of his animadversions on Gurney's boiler it is ironic that Maceroni's was also a water-tube affair. It was, however, very different and in its first form contained eighty-one vertical tubes, arranged in nine rows in a horseshoe formation about the firebox. The bottom water connections between rows of tubes served as fire-bars and, by keeping them cool, the water, helped to prevent clinkering. A steam-dome helped prevent priming and the boiler was very quick-steaming; it was regularly worked at 150–200 p.s.i. which was considerably above Gurney's normal working pressure, and this no doubt accounts for Maceroni's $7\frac{1}{2}$ inches by $15\frac{1}{2}$ inches engine giving as much power as Gurney's 9 inches by 18 inches. Apart from the boiler, and a very modern-looking chassis upswept over the unsprung driving-axle, Maceroni's vehicles exhibited no startling novelties of design and, as we have seen, he suffered as much as his contemporaries from crank-axle breakages. All the controls were under the steersman's command, no third man was needed and the automatic engine lubrication was much in advance of the time.

It would be unjust to leave this brief account of those who so nearly succeeded without some reference to W. H. James, whose father won distinction as a railway engineer and whose most ambitious and advanced design of 1832 was never built, but provides, nevertheless, a noteworthy example of ingenious pre-Victorian technology.

James's first steam-carriage experiments go back to 1823, when he patented a high-pressure water-tube boiler expressly designed for carriage work. In 1824–5 he constructed a 'drag' with two separate two-cylinder engines, of very small dimensions by 1825 standards, each of which drove one back wheel. This method of overcoming the differential difficulty was revived by Amédée Bollée some forty years later on his famous steam bus *L'Obéissante*; but James fitted an additional refinement in the shape of a control mechanism, coupled to the steering-gear, which reduced steam to the inside wheel, and increased the supply to the outside one when cornering.

In 1829 a large coach with rather similar machinery was financed by Sir James Anderson. This had two of James's patent boilers and the working pressure was no less than 250 p.s.i., which showed up the weaknesses of pre-Victorian metallurgy. It is recorded in Galloway's *History of the Steam Engine,* published in 1830, that ordinary gas piping was used for the boiler tubes and either they or the jointed steam connections persistently gave way. Even so the big three-ton coach gave quite a good account of itself, and on one occasion carried twenty passengers at ten miles an hour using only one boiler, after the other had split a tube and extinguished its fire. The coach was soon dismantled and the engines used for another 'drag' fitted with *four* small boilers which had stronger tubes made of better material. Unhappily this tempted the designer into the folly of raising the working pressure to 300 p.s.i., which was, once again, too much for the materials.

The 1832 design of 'drag', shown in Plate 26, was altogether different, and if Sir James Anderson had not temporarily withdrawn from the steam-coach arena it would have been put on the road in 1833. It had only one boiler, designed for a relatively modest 200 p.s.i., with one twin-cylinder engine mounted diagonally over it. The most striking feature of the vehicle is the three-speed gear, which is of the type used to such good effect a century later by Frazer-Nash. This not only allowed the use of a smaller engine than would have been needed for a single-ratio transmission (on which a wastefully large reserve of power must always be provided), but was arranged to allow gear-changing to be done with the vehicle in motion. This most desirable attribute was not to be found on the traction engines of seventy years later.

The motion was taken from the crankshaft by sprocket wheels and pitch-chains. The chain wheels were of different sizes, to provide the different ratios, and those on the countershaft were selectively clutched to it by pedal-operated claw clutches with a neat interlock mechanism which released one clutch before another was engaged. By momentarily shutting off steam and pressing the appropriate pedal the gear could be changed without undue jerk or snatch at the chain and, for the first time, the driver was also to be provided with a footbrake. Final drive was by side-chains, in the manner common on motor cars many years later, and the back axle therefore could be hung on springs. The final-drive sprockets on the countershaft were connected to it by friction clutches * controlled by the steering-gear in such a way that the inside wheel was disconnected when cornering. This may have been a somewhat crude substitute for a differential gear, but at least it was better than the usual arrangements of James's contemporaries. The specification included a condenser to conserve water, feed-water heater and gas-lighting. Given reasonable luck with the boiler, this 'drag', had it ever been built, must have been the most practicable of all those designed before 1840.

Apart from some isolated experiments which led nowhere, little was done between 1840 and 1860. When the 'steam on common roads' question again attracted attention the railways were firmly entrenched and, if one disregards a few attractive by-ways, the path trodden between 1860 and 1880 led to the traction engine, which, though an impressive beast and a useful beast, was a slow and cumbersome beast by comparison with some of its ancestors.

The traction engine of the late nineteenth century, which was still in production, little altered, into the nineteen-twenties, was primarily a child of the 'portable' or agricultural engine, which was not self-propelling in its original form. 'Portable' is something of a misnomer for a piece of machinery weighing two to three tons, but the name was used for a steam engine and boiler on wheels, with a swivelling forecarriage and shafts so that it could be moved by horsepower. Engines of this sort were well established by the middle eighteen-forties, and the most favoured layout comprised a horizontal, locomotive-type, fire-tube boiler with a tall folding smoke stack and a single-cylinder horizontal engine mounted on top of the

* Described (and condemned) by most nineteenth-century writers as ratchet clutches, which, they say, would not have been satisfactory. Had ratchet clutches been used, the outside wheel would automatically have overrun the inner one and the connections to the steering-gear would not have been needed. Patent specification drawings show friction clutches.

boiler casing. About 4 h.p. was the usual output and these machines were used for driving threshing or chaff-cutting machines and other agricultural purposes; they were also occasionally used on large construction works to provide power for derricks or pile-drivers.

It was so obvious and easy a step to make the portable engine self-moving, with chain or gear transmission, that this began to be common practice before 1860. At first, the self-moving property was the only desideratum and the first engines of this sort retained the shafts and were steered by a pilot horse. This rather bizarre arrangement soon gave way to a pilot-wheel system such as Gurney had used, and then to the familiar chain steering-gear worked by a hand wheel from the footplate. The transition from an engine which could move itself from one work-site to another into one which could haul a load was natural, though agricultural work remained the primary task of the traction engine in the mid-nineteenth century.

There was an alien strain in this evolution and a number of 'road locomotives', expressly designed as such, appeared in the 1860s which did not derive from the 'portables'. Although the 'traction engine', as we know it, was officially titled a 'road locomotive', it will be convenient to keep this designation for the engines of this middle period.

Figure 12 Carrett steam carriage 1862

There was also a sprinkling of private 'steam carriages' of this era which were uneasy compromises between railway locomotives and wagonettes. Carrett's steam carriage, so called, of 1862 is a good example which performed very well, though it is at once apparent that, in many ways, it is a clumsy and primitive conveyance by comparison with some of its predecessors. Though it had room for only seven or eight passengers it weighed five tons, which was considerably more than Hancock's twenty-two-seater *Automaton*. A stout wrist must have been needed to control the tiller steering of this elephantine three-wheeler.

Some other passenger vehicles in this *genre* were rather less ponderous, though still too much like a shunting-engine out on a spree to offer much threat to the horse-carriage trade. A sprightly four-wheeler, built in the same year as the Carrett, was Tangye's *Cornubia*, which is not only interesting in itself but because of the reason for its construction. In his autobiography, *One and All*, Richard Tangye wrote:

> About 1862 the subject of providing 'feeders' in country places for the main lines of railway came into prominence. Branch lines had been proved to be unremunerative from their great cost in construction; and amongst other systems proposed was that of light, quick-speed locomotives for carrying passengers, and traction engines for the conveyance of . . . goods. We determined to construct a locomotive of the former class, and succeeded in making a very successful example, with which we travelled many hundreds of miles. The carriage . . . when travelling at over twenty miles an hour . . . was easily managed and under perfect control.
>
> . . . It soon became evident that there was an opening for a considerable business in these engines, and we made our preparations accordingly, but the 'wisdom' of Parliament made it impossible . . . Although a judge ruled that a horse that would not stand the sight or sound of a locomotive, in these days of steam, constituted a public danger, and that its owner should be punished and not the owner of the locomotive, an Act was passed providing that no engine should travel more than four miles an hour on the public roads. Thus was the trade in quick-speed locomotives strangled in its cradle, and the inhabitants of country districts left unprovided with improved facilities for travelling.

Parliament's 'wisdom' in this connection had first been expressed in 24 & 25 Vic., c. 70, of 1861, which, as we have seen (Chapter 3), was by no means discouraging, as it was partly concerned with the removal of discriminatory tolls. Presumably it was this which put the steam-traction opponents on their guard, and just as the stage-coach proprietors of 1820–30 had indirectly worked upon the turn-pike trusts to impose the tolls so, it is fair to assume, did the railway interests of 1865 combine with other forces (no doubt behind the scenes and tacitly) to bring about the framing and passing of 28 & 29 Vic., c. 83, four years later. It was this piece of legislative folly which held back progress for a generation: but in the light of its time it was not wholly unreasonable beyond suffering the fatal weakness, common to most legislation dealing with technical matters, of assuming that engineering techniques would stay frozen at the point then existing. The assumption itself, once enshrined in an Act of Parliament, ensures the continuance of the frost.

If one takes into account the nature of road surfaces in 1865 and the very great weights involved, it was not unreasonable to put a speed limit on mechanical vehicles. It was unreasonable, however, not to provide for less burdensome restrictions on vehicles below a certain weight in order to provide an incentive to designers to reduce their customers' fuel bills at the same time as reducing wear on the roads. If one remembers that the traffic in towns was already dense and that most of the horses were controlled by drivers whose ineptitude was reflected in the nervousness of their beasts at the sight of anything unusual, from a blown newspaper to a steam engine, then it was not unreasonable to stipulate that, in certain areas, 'road locomotives' should be preceded by the 'man with the red flag'. Obviously, this entailed fixing the speed limit at a walking pace, instead of the 8–12 m.p.h. that most of the engine designers recommended. The folly of this clause lay in making the walking attendant as obligatory on a deserted road in the remote Highlands as he was in Oxford Street. Also, if one considers that all the road locomotives of the 1860s were designed to be worked by two men, then it was not unreasonable to stipulate that two men (in addition to the walking attendant) must always be present; but by failing to provide for possible developments this clause removed any incentive for an ingenious engineer to design hopper-fed furnaces and thermo-static devices to make boilers self-regulating.

The worst aspect of the 1865 Act was that it created a repressive climate which encouraged those who were hostile to the horseless carriage; and the general feeling of 1865 was curiously but indisputably more hostile than that of 1830. Many factors contributed to this and the widespread popularity of railway shares amongst the respectable middle class (recovered from the boom and collapse of the 'forties) doubtless played a part. Also, Victorian society was an acquisitive one to which the carriage-and-pair was a status symbol *par excellence*. How many impoverished elderly gentlefolk in this century have consoled themselves with the thought that 'papa kept his carriage, you know' as they struggled to keep up appearances? As many positions of local authority, including the magisterial bench, were occupied by those who had only recently risen to carriage-keeping status, it can be seen why vexatious prosecutions for trifling misdemeanours became part of the motoring scene long before the motor car, as we know it, existed. Mr George Salt, the owner of the 1862 Carrett steam carriage, was so discouraged by the 1865 Act he gave it to Frederick Hodges, a noted steam-engine enthusiast, who christened it the *Fly-by-Night* because he used it only by night in order not to inconvenience others; nevertheless, he was prosecuted six times in as many weeks, although there had been no complaints.

One result of this legislation was to make the British motor industry an export business before any significant home market existed. Between 1865 and 1885 English-made road locomotives hauled passenger or goods vehicles in Russia, Turkey, Greece, Spain, Portugal, France, Ceylon and, most notably, India; even Richard Tangye's *Cornubia* ended its days as the 'motor car' of a Turkish pasha. The use of road engines for heavy work slowly developed at home, but, broadly speaking, the home trade in road traction engines did not amount to much before 1880. This concentration of effort upon slow, heavy vehicles left the door open for France and Germany to take the lead in establishing the light motor vehicle.

As we have seen in Chapter 5, Robert Thompson, the inventor of the pneumatic tyre, designed a road locomotive in 1861 on which he used solid rubber tyres. Locomotives of his type occupy a central position in the evolution of the traction engine and were made by a number of famous firms, some of whom are still in the heavy lorry business. Amongst them were those noted East Anglian concerns, Ransomes, Sims and Jefferies of Ipswich, makers of the first self-moving agricultural engine, and Charles Burrell and Sons of Thetford, whose splendid showmen's engines of the early twentieth century mark the apogee of the steam traction engine.

In its original form the Thompson locomotive was a three-wheeler (as were the majority during this intermediate period), with the

Figure 13 Burrell's version of Thompson's road steamer

wrought-iron chassis framing passing outside the single front wheel, which was steered by worm-and-wheel gear. The engines were of six nominal horsepower and the locomotives weighed between five and six tons, and on a trial in 1869 one of them hauled thirty-four tons up a one in eighteen incline. The only component of these machines which was unsatisfactory was the one of which the designer was most proud—his patent vertical 'pot' boiler. After repeated modifications had failed to cure its deficiencies, most of the firms who made Thompson steamers used vertical Field boilers (these gave excellent results on the Thompson steamers used in India); but in 1871 Burrell and Co. brought out a modified Thompson engine with a railway-type horizontal fire-tube boiler.

Burrell also later replaced the single twelve-inch wide front wheel
by a pair of narrower ones on a short axle which could still be accommodated in the width of the framing. Although the differential gear
was now quite well known, it was not used, and one of the final drive
pinions on the countershaft had to be thrown out of gear on sharp
curves. Sliding pinions and gear wheels provided for a low and a high
speed, and there were four separate levers to control the gear-
changing and cornering arrangements. With the steam regulator
and variable cut-off to look after as well, and with very low-geared
steering, the driver had plenty to do; but the stoker had command of
the solitary brake and could also tilt the boiler and firebox bodily, by
means of a gargantuan worm and rack device, in order to avoid
leaving the crown of the firebox uncovered by water when climbing
steep hills—for the firebox end of the boiler faced the direction of
travel. The risk of leaving the firebox crown uncovered was often
put forward as a reason why the rail-locomotive type of boiler would
not be suitable for road locomotives, but Burrell's adjustable firebox
was soon found to be an unnecessary complication.

The Burrell-Thompson type of engine gave good service but with
the boiler 'hind side before' it was awkward to fire, and by 1880, in
common with most other firms in the business, Burrells reverted to
the agricultural or portable engine layout; and nearly all the traction
engines (and road rollers) made during the next forty years followed
this plan with such improvements and patented features as the experience and ingenuity of their manufacturers dictated.

The Highways and Locomotives Act of 1878 (14 & 42 Vic., c. 77)
abolished the financial autonomy of the parishes, and increased the
standing of the highway districts by providing that their funds
should come from a common highway rate and that theirs should be
the sole authority in determining where and how the money should
be spent. At the same time the new Act re-defined most of the regulations governing road locomotives and gave to the local bodies
increased powers to impose any further restrictions they thought
appropriate. In many localities traction engines were altogether ban-
ned during daylight hours (the Act specified that they must be
allowed eight consecutive working hours in each twenty-four) and
nearly all authorities took full advantage of the power to 'recover
expenses caused by excessive weight and extraordinary traffic'. As
Mr Aveling, of Aveling and Porter, the famous traction-engine

CHARLES BURRELL & SONS, LTD.

PATENT

SPRING MOUNTED ROAD LOCOMOTIVES.

WE have now 60 Engines at work fitted with our Patent Spring arrangement, giving most excellent results, and the demand for them is steadily increasing, since users of Traction Engines are beginning to appreciate a saving of **50 per cent.** in the wear and tear of the Engine which this system effects

This arrangement is considered by all who have seen it, and ridden on the Engines thus fitted, to be the only practical solution of the difficulty which has hitherto existed, of mounting Geared Traction Engines upon springs **without additional complication.** Since it does not increase the number of wearing parts, and there are no parts either to wear out, nor does it alter the design of the Engine in any way.

St. Nicholas Works, THETFORD, Norfolk.

Figure 14 Period advertisement showing typical traction engine of the 1890s

27 The Grenville Steam Carriage, 1875

28 1903 Lanchester

29 Iron plate on stone pillar at White Post, Somerset, erected by the Bath Trust

30 A cast iron mile post erected at Kilmersdon by the Radstock Turnpike Trust c. 1800

31 The Stanton Drew Toll-house in Somerset
(West Harptree Trust)

makers observed: '. . . if I send a boiler weighing fifteen tons drawn by fifteen horses (weighing eight tons) over a bridge and that boiler breaks the bridge, I have nothing to pay, but if I send the same boiler over the bridge drawn by an engine (weighing eight tons), and that boiler breaks through the bridge, I have the whole expenses to pay.'

The local authorities were also very unreasonable about allowing engine drivers to draw water from wayside streams or ponds; apart from these and other locally imposed restrictions the Act also established the right of every person in charge of a horse to order an engine to stop at his behest, for as long as was necessary to allow the animal to be guided out of sight and sound of the monster, no matter how inconvenient or dangerous this might be to the engine driver. Dangerous, because the Act also included one of those fatuous clauses so beloved of the legislature when they attempt to regulate technical matters. This clause stated: 'Nor shall the steam be allowed to attain a pressure such as to exceed the limit fixed by the safety valve, so that no steam shall blow off when the locomotive is upon the road.' If it had been enacted that no locomotive driver should open the cylinder drain cocks, or otherwise allow his engine to blow off steam unreasonably or in a deliberately vexatious way, nobody could have objected, but with its usual dislike of leaving anything to common sense Parliament made a rule which, in many instances, drivers could only keep by tampering with their safety valves. William Fletcher[5] wrote:

. . . the driver has just replenished his fire in readiness for mounting a hill . . . and as the fire brightens up and the steam approaches maximum working pressure . . . a carriage and pair appear in the distance. The engine is stopped to allow the equipage to pass, which, however, with the horses generally harnessed to gentlemen's carriages, is no easy matter and while the animals are prancing and plunging . . . the pressure gauge pointer travels fast, notwithstanding that the driver has closed the damper and opened the fire door; and the only alternative is to allow the steam to blow off and thus break the law, or keep the law by wedging down the spring balance to a dangerous degree . . . To comply with this piece of Parliamentary wisdom it is necessary to retain the steam in the boiler, thereby placing lives of human beings in

. . . the greatest peril from an explosion, so that horses shall not be frightened by steam issuing from the safety valve.

Fifty years' experience of railways had shown that properly handled horses could work in goods yards and railway sidings without turning a hair, though locomotives snorted and clanked on every side; but just as the 'lady bicyclists' of the late 'nineties felt it was due to their sensitivity to fall off if they heard the sound of a motor engine, so did many horsemen grow incensed at the sight of a mechanical vehicle to such a degree that they gave vent to their feelings by shouting and sawing at the reins, which inevitably made their horses nervous.

Despite all the restrictions, traction engines multiplied rapidly as their sheer utility and economy became apparent. On the score of weight and speed the road engine of the 'nineties may have seemed a poor article by comparison with the steam coaches or 'drags' of the 'thirties, but it scored heavily for reliability and economy. The very great weight of the fire-tube boiler was partly offset by its rigidity, which made a separate chassis frame unnecessary; and in all other details as there was no incentive to save weight there was no temptation to skimp safety margins—indeed, many parts were quite unnecessarily massive. Finally, although average working pressures were little higher than they had been sixty years earlier, the extra efficiency gained from the use of a variable cut-off, better valve gear, better proportions of steam pipes and ports and, very often, by compounding was remarkable.

Though the horse-loving gentry might snort as loudly as the traction engines they detested, it could not be denied that one engine could do the work of a dozen or more horses. No matter how avidly 'authority' in all its guises might emulate Mrs Partington, the next phase in the evolution of transport could not be held back.

The Horseless Carriage Triumphant

It is sometimes suggested that the restrictions in Great Britain resulted in the light internal-combustion motor car being a Continental rather than a British invention. Whilst it is certainly true that we had lost ground badly after the excellent start of the 1830s, and that Continental designers and manufacturers were given a head start by the restrictions, it is by no means certain that the petrol-engined car would have been born in this country had the 1865 Act never been passed. The abundance, in those days, of cheap coal, and the great British investment of capital and engineering talent in the steam engine have also to be taken into account. It is also true that several manufacturing concerns, in anticipation or more vague hope of some liberalizing legislation, began in the early 1890s to take a new look at the lumbering traction engine, and to sketch plans for some lighter and swifter, but still steam-driven, successor.

The history of the motor car has been written and rewritten so many times in recent years that, although much which has been published is inaccurate to the verge of the ludicrous, there is no lack of material, and it is only necessary here to draw the essential features in outline.

The first commercially practicable gas engine was patented by Etienne Lenoir in 1860: although inefficient, the Lenoir engines were so simple and reliable that they were made in fair numbers, in many countries, until nearly the end of the century or for some twenty years after more efficient designs had been put on the market. The first commercially practicable four-stroke gas engine was devised by Gottlieb Daimler, on behalf of his employers, Otto and Langen, in 1876. In 1885 Daimler, now working on his own behalf, with Wilhelm Maybach as his assistant, patented a small, vertical, self-contained, high-speed (700 r.p.m.) engine expressly designed for use with liquid fuel. This was the direct ancestor of the modern four-stroke motor engine.

Between 1860 and 1885 a few internal-combustion vehicles were produced—Lenoir himself made one in 1862–3—but these were isolated experiments which led nowhere, although the Markus motor car of 1874–5 was worthy of development. Late in 1884 Carl Benz, a gas-engine manufacturer in a small way, began his attempts to cross-breed a scaled-down horizontal gas engine, with electric ignition and a surface vaporizer, with a large two-seat tricycle. The first child born of this improbable marriage made its first trial run in the spring of 1885. Improved tri-cars on the same general plan followed in 1886–7, and in 1886, also, Daimler and Maybach demonstrated a crude wooden bicycle and an equally crude converted horse-carriage propelled by the Daimler engine. At about the time of Benz's first attempt Edward Butler in England designed and made a petrol-engined tricycle, which he altered and improved considerably during the next two years before deciding that it had no commercial future because of the restrictions. In 1887 Benz sold his third (or fourth) three-wheeler to Emile Roger of Paris, and at the same time granted him sales and manufacturing rights for France. The modern motor industry had started: hitherto the only motorists had been the inventors themselves, but from early 1888 onwards any member of the public so foolhardy and so lost to all sense of decency as to wish for a horseless carriage could go to Roger in Paris or Benz in Mannheim and order one.

Whilst these things were going on in the internal-combustion field the light steam vehicle was not being neglected. There were some notable Italian contributions, but, again, the principal men in this sphere were French and included Amédee Bollée, senior, De Dion, Bouton et Trépardoux and Léon Serpollet, who, in 1889, re-invented the 'flash boiler' or instantaneous steam generator which had been tried (similar in principal though different in form) in the Burstall and Hill steam coach of 1824. The principal difference between the boilers was that Serpollet's worked well whilst Burstall and Hill's did not: another Burstall and Hill feature which came into its own many years later was a system of four-wheel drive, using a longitudinal propeller shaft and bevel gearing.

In 1889 French manufacturing rights in the Daimler engines were granted to Messrs Panhard et Levassor, and in 1891 Emile

Levassor designed the type of motor car with a forward-mounted vertical engine, pedal-controlled friction clutch and sliding-pinion change-speed gear which set the pattern for the conventional motor car of the twentieth century. The Daimler Motoren Geselleschaft was formed in November 1890 and the following year saw a considerable expansion of the Benz business, with the introduction of a four-wheeled version of his rear-engined belt-driven carriage which, though made in different sizes, remained in production essentially unaltered for ten years. Motor historians have argued that this was a manifestation of Benz's ineradicable obstinacy, without seeing that it was also a manifestation of a possibly primitive but remarkably reliable and deservedly successful design. Though the Panhard-Levassor, Peugeot and other designs of the early 'nineties may have been more 'modern' in concept, the simple Benz exactly suited the conditions of the time: it was copied, either under licence or by piracy, by a number of French and, in due time, English manufacturers.

Between 1890 and 1895 the motor car developed quickly in France, rather less quickly in Germany and virtually not at all in America or Great Britain. Motoring as a properly organized sport was firmly established in France by the Paris–Rouen Trial of 1894 and by the ambitious Paris–Bordeaux–Paris Race of 1895. This saw the resounding success of Emile Levassor, who drove his two-cylinder $3\frac{1}{2}$ h.p. car, single-handed, for $48\frac{3}{4}$ hours to cover the 732 miles at an average speed of 15 m.p.h. This not only showed M. Levassor to be a man of extraordinary stamina but, to those who would see, it also established the light petrol motor car as something much more important than a mechanical toy for rich eccentrics.

There were those in England who could see, and many of them had been trying for some time to open governmental eyes. These efforts not only came from those concerned with heavy steam transport, but from a growing number of enthusiasts and amateurs (in the best sense) who became interested in the newfangled French and German horseless carriages.

Two who were particularly active, and well placed to influence opinion, were the Hon. Evelyn Ellis and Sir David Salomons, both of whom brought motor cars from France (a Panhard-Levassor and a Peugeot respectively) for use in England in defiance of the regulations in order to demonstrate their absurdity. Evelyn Ellis deliberately courted prosecution by frequently driving through Windsor at 12–14 m.p.h., but his scheme misfired: he was so well known and his family connections (he was a son of Lord Howard de Walden) were so influential in Government circles that the police left him alone: but the lectures and public demonstrations he gave helped overcome opposition. Sir David Salomons also spoke and wrote, founded and organized the Self-Propelled Traffic Association and on 15 October 1895 held England's first Motor Show at his house near Tunbridge Wells. It is true that he could only muster six exhibits, but the affair was well publicized and attended, and the leading papers carried enthusiastic accounts of the ease and speed with which the machines had darted about the drives and paddocks of Sir David's estate.

Towards the autumn of 1895 it became known that negotiations were going on between the Home Office, the Local Government Board, the Self-Propelled Traffic Association and other interested parties; a handful more motor cars were imported from the Continent, established engineering concerns hastened their plans to produce 'light' steam 'lurries' (as the spelling then was) as alternatives to the heavy traction engines, two or three engineers addressed themselves to motor-car design and there were stirrings and rumblings in the business world mostly centred upon the serio-comic activities of one H. J. Lawson. The negotiations bore rather meagre fruit in the Locomotives on Highways Act (61 & 62 Vic., c. 29), which received the royal assent in June 1896, but which, with typical overcaution, was not brought into effect until 14 November. As the measure was introduced as a Government Bill, and as few members showed the slightest interest in it (the majority clearly thinking that the handful of cranks they presumed it was intended to appease would soon lose interest in their new toys), it passed both Houses without difficulty.

Except for being less liberal and far-sighted about speeds, the 1896 Act was almost wholly based on the recommendations of the Select Committee on Locomotives on Roads, whose expertly stated report in 1873 had been totally ignored by the House when the Act of 1878 was framed, debated and passed. The eagerness Parliament shows in devoting time and money to setting up select committees of conscientious members to weigh the best available opinions is always matched by an equal readiness to ignore their findings. The 1896 Act did too little too late, and left too many loopholes through which the Local Government Board could frustrate its intentions. Thus the maximum speed set by the Act was '14 m.p.h. or less than this as the Local Government Board may decide', and the board promptly decided that the difference between 14 m.p.h. and 12 m.p.h. spelled the difference between safety and danger. As finally regulated by the Board the speeds were:

Weight unladen:	Under 1½ tons	Over 1½ tons	Over 2 tons
Maximum speed:	12 m.p.h.	8 m.p.h.	5 m.p.h.

After consultation with the board, individual local authorities were given power, which was widely exercised, to set local speed limits lower still, but at least the regulations recognized, as the 1873 Committee had urged, that what was proper for a ten-ton locomotive was not necessarily proper for a five-hundredweight tricycle.

All vehicles with a tare weight of less than three tons were now exempt from the 'three persons in attendance' rule, but some of the technical provisions were as daft as such things generally are. The tare weight, for example, was to be calculated without fuel and water, which, for a three-ton-tare steam lorry of that time would have been, on average, about another thirty hundredweight; but the batteries of an electric vehicle were classed as 'fuel', so a three-ton electric vehicle could have had another three or more tons of accumulators in place and still have qualified as a 'light locomotive' within the meaning of the Act.

Parliament and the Local Government Board also went into quite unnecessary detail about tyre widths in relation to weight, which would have been much better settled by experience and corrected by the common law if damage was caused. These regulations made little sense in the case of steel tyres and no sense at all in relation to the solid rubber or pneumatic tyres which were almost universal for all but the old heavy traction engines. As Worby Beaumont pointed out, the width of pneumatics was immaterial as far as rut forming was concerned, and no heavy-vehicle manufacturer who valued his reputation would fit solid rubber tyres too narrow for the load; and if he overcautiously made them wider than was necessary it was no concern of Parliament. As is nearly always the case with technical Bills, those who drafted the Act cloaked their ignorance in language of sybilline obscurity: they specified in connection with pneumatic tyres, or tyres of soft material, that the width as calculated was to be the width when not subject to pressure, though the measurement was to be made at the point where the tyre touched the road. One trusts that this clause did not mean what it said.

Despite all its absurdities, the Act made motoring possible, but by the time any significant number of private or light commercial vehicles had taken the road as a result of its provisions it could be seen that it was already out of date. At least it was a start, and one of the first to take advantage of it was H. J. Lawson. This extraordinary man, part visionary, part charlatan, liked to think of himself as the 'Father of the British Motor Industry', but as maternity is a matter of fact and paternity only a matter of opinion his role was much more that of wicked fairy godfather at the christening.

Lawson's forte lay in the shadier areas of company promotion, but he had a nodding acquaintance with engineering methods (he was the patentee of the Lawson Safety Bicycle) and he saw clearly that mechanical road transport was going to grow into a huge industry. He had made a fortune out of company promotions, mergers and share juggling in the cycle trade, and he determined to control the unborn motor industry by similar methods.

With two somewhat unsavoury associates, the notorious Martin Rucker and Terrence Hooley (who was later jailed for a Stock Exchange fraud), he set up the British Motor Syndicate Ltd early in 1895. The Syndicate's first move was to buy the agency and manufacturing rights in the Daimler and Maybach patents from the English licensee, Frederick Simms, who had conducted a small trade in Daimler engines for river launches and similar work since 1893. Having bought out Simms's *Daimler Motor Syndicate* for £35,000, Lawson set up the *Daimler Motor Company Ltd*, in January 1896, with himself and his nominees on the board, and promptly organized the purchase from his British Motor Syndicate of the Daimler rights for £40,000. This process was repeated many times; every available motor patent was bought, usually at an inflated price calculated to impress the shareholders, and manufacturing rights were then sold or leased to existing cycle companies already controlled by Lawson; or to new motor manufacturing companies set up for the purpose, such as the grandiose Great Horseless Carriage Company which was capitalized at £750,000 and never produced a motor vehicle before it was reorganized, at great loss to the shareholders, as the Motor Manufacturing Company in 1897.

The British Motor Syndicate made a handsome profit on each transaction and the fact that many of the patents, such as the Pennington for which £100,000 was paid, were worthless mattered little to Lawson. He and his cronies, sitting on the boards of the different companies, were not only entitled to their directors' fees but were able to stave off the day or reckoning.

It was a cosy set-up, paralleled in America a few years later by similar manoeuvres over the Selden patent, but it delayed the proper development of the industry which Lawson genuinely desired to see flourishing. It created a great deal of ill-will; it inhibited many genuine concerns by threatening or instituting litigation over alleged infringement of patents and by the end of the century it had made the whole motor business stink in the nostrils of the financial world, so that genuine concerns had great difficulty in raising capital.

All these activities were accompanied by Barnum and Bailey type showmanship and publicity. According to the advertisements every type of motor vehicle from a ½ h.p. bicycle to a four-ton lorry was available from one or another of the group's companies immediately after the 1896 Act took effect. In fact, it is doubtful whether any English cars were made under Lawson's aegis until at least a year later. Some so-called English cars were sold by the Coventry Daimler Company (so called then to distinguish it from the original German concern) early in 1897, but they were imported Cannstatt-Daimlers disguised with English name plates. Similarly the Beeston Motor Tricycle which ran in Lawson's 'Emancipation Day' celebration run from London to Brighton was really a De Dion Bouton and the first Coventry Motettes were imported Léon Bollées. The Emancipation Day Run was compounded, as most of Lawson's affairs were, of equal parts of chaos, puffing and farce. Only those makes in which he had a financial interest were included in the official list of finishers —but this list does include the Bersey electric carriage, which made most of the journey by courtesy of the London, Brighton and South Coast Railway Co. The Run did much more harm than good to the motoring cause.

It was always vehemently asserted that machines sold by Lawson's companies were 'British throughout', but even the Daimler Company made use, at first, of many imported components; it is known that as late as 1899 an uninspired belt-driven voiturette of poor design and

execrable performance, the Critchley Daimler, was put into production expressly to use up a stock of obsolete German engines. The
larger Daimler models were closely modelled on Panhard-Levassor,
and in spite of constant board-room squabbles, near-bankruptcy and
financial storms the English Daimler Company had earned its reputation for good quality before the end of the century.

Either in defiance of Lawson's Syndicate, or by knuckling under
and paying royalties, some agencies were set up to import cars. The
Benz patents lay outside his control, and the most successful import-
ing business was conducted by Henry Hewetson, who had the Benz
agency. In due time English companies, notably the Star Manufacturing Co. of Wolverhampton, began making Benz-type cars in
this country; and in the last year of the century a number of firms
were turning out tricycles, tricars or quads made from imported
components and mostly relying on the admirable De Dion Bouton
engines. Quite a number of these concerns faded quickly from the
scene, but some of them, such as Dennis Bros of Guildford, went on
to develop their own designs of motor cars and lorries.

Some wholly native efforts were also started before the 1896 Act
took effect; most were isolated experiments, like the Roots, the
Knight and the Bremer, which led nowhere; but an important exception was the Lanchester, Britain's first four-wheeled* petrol car
of wholly native design, which made its first trial run in February
1896. From this prototype, which was soon modified by the installation of a twin-cylinder, double-crankshaft, vibrationless engine, epi-
cyclic gearbox and Lanchester's famous enveloping worm gear,
Frederick and George Lanchester evolved two improved cars which
formed the basis for their first production model of 1900 to 1905.
As an example of original design, which owed nothing to existing
sources (most contemporary designs borrowed freely from the cycle
and carriage trades), the Lanchester was a brilliant conception.[1]

Soon after the Lanchester had made its first run Herbert Austin
produced an experimental tri-car for his employers, the Wolseley
Sheep Shearing Machine Company. This was obviously based on the
Léon Bollée and was not satisfactory, but Austin went on to design

---

* The Roots and the Knight were designed as tri-cars, though the Knight
was subsequently rebuilt as a four-wheeler. The Bremer certainly antedates
the Lanchester as a 'native' four-wheeled petrol car, but as it is obviously a
very crude copy of a Benz it scarcely qualifies for the title of British.

an improved tri-car and then, in 1899, a four-wheeled belt-driven voiturette which formed the basis for a model which went into production, like the Lanchester, late in 1900. A third most important newcomer to motor manufacture was Montagu Napier, who had been employed in 1898 by S. F. Edge, a brilliant entrepreneur then working as Dunlop's London Manager, to modernize an old-pattern Panhard-Levassor by converting it from tiller to wheel steering. From this Napier had gone on to design a new engine, and the first complete Napier car, still recognizably Panhard-Levassor in origin, was finished just in time to take part with distinction in the Automobile Club's 1,000 Miles Trial in April 1900.

Governmental grandmotherliness and Lawsonian sophistry stunted the infancy of the private-car industry, but by the time of the 1,000 Miles Trial most of Lawson's empire was in decay and the infant began to thrive. Of the three principal pioneers two were bolstered from extraneous sources; the motor-vehicle part of Napier's business (soon the principal and then the only part) was in the hands of S. F. Edge, who was supported by the powerful Du Cros family, and they in turn controlled the Dunlop business and had extensive omnibus, cab and cycle interests; the Wolseley Tool and Motor Co. became part of the vast Vickers group, but the Lanchester Engine Co. struggled on, independent and under-capitalized. The industry grew quickly, not only in numbers engaged and output, but in establishing a definite British flavour. One must stress British rather than English here, as three of the leading firms, Argyll, Arrol-Johnston and Albion, were Scottish.

Continental cars, mostly French, continued to dominate the motor scene for the first four or five years of the century, but it was to some extent a two-way traffic, as British capital played quite a large part in the French industry, and most of the imported cars, except in the voiturette class, were imported as bare chassis and equipped with English coachwork and accessories. As early as 1897, indeed, Hewetson had supplied his Benz cars with Brampton driving-chains and Connolly tyres in place of the German ones, which he found unreliable.

Many small firms assembled French components into complete cars and gave the resultant confections resoundingly British names such as Marlborough, Sandringham or Stirling; most of these were voiturettes with single-cylinder engines (generally De Dion Bouton), but some of the larger Continental cars were also copied here. In 1903, for example, the Earl of Shrewsbury and Talbot (that same nobleman who had put London's first rubber-tyred hansom cabs on the streets in 1885) financed and organized a company to make Clément cars under licence. A splendid factory was equipped with the latest machinery, and the first cars made at Ladbroke Grove were identical with their French counterparts and were known as Clement-Talbots; but within a few months distinctive home-brewed designs were put in hand and the 'Clement' was dropped from the name. Similarly the first four-cylinder Sunbeams were really Berliets, the Crossley was based on Mercedes, the Weigel on Itala and so on.

The majority of motor-manufacturing concerns to spring up in the early years owed nothing to foreign influence, however, and British influence on design soon began to flow back across the Channel: the bias was towards refinement. English carriage-work had long been admired for elegance and luxury, and the British motor manufacturers at the upper end of the scale soon began to cater for their customers' traditional insistence upon that indefinable something known as quality. Although many Englishmen were prominent in motor-racing circles from the beginning, and English racing cars began to make their mark when a Napier won the 1902 Gordon Bennett Race, the carriage-gentry customers valued silence, comfort, smooth running and good suspension and road-holding above outright speed. The general speed limit, which was raised to 20 m.p.h. by the Motor Car Act of 1903 (3 Edw. VII, c. 36), also had its effect in promoting a bias. The first six-cylinder car, a Spyker, was exhibited in the autumn of 1903, but the makers did not persevere with it, and it was Napier, urged by the tireless and sometimes absurd campaigning of S. F. Edge, who made the six-cylinder car a commercial proposition. It was Dr Lanchester who conquered the torsional vibration bogy which haunted most early six-cylinder engines and it was Rolls-Royce, relative newcomers to the trade, who produced in the Silver Ghost (which went into production at the rate of four chassis a week in 1907) a car which set world standards of refinement, economy and reliability for two decades. It is wrong to assume, as many have done, that the Rolls-Royces, Lanchesters, Napiers, Sheffield-Simplexes and other 'luxury' cars sacrificed performance in the quest for silence and smoothness: seen through the eyes of the time they were also fast cars.

The motor car aroused fierce opposition; there is no doubt that many pioneer motorists were foolhardy and inconsiderate cads who took apparent pleasure in splashing innoffensive walkers with mud, forcing bicyclists into the gutter and terrifying old ladies out of their wits. Even the considerate drivers could not avoid raising dust in dry weather, and this was a very genuine source of grievance before road surfaces were sealed. Much of the opposition stemmed, however, from the dislike of innovation which had grown on the British public towards the end of the nineteenth century, and from the exaggerated class consciousness of Edwardian England. Carriages were kept by gentlefolk and gentlefolk did not associate with engineers, whom they considered to be illiterate and grease-stained boors; therefore those who drove horseless carriages were no better than artisans. Another facet of this attitude was that middle- and lower-middle-class persons were trying to edge into the ranks of the carriage folk by the back door of horseless-carriage ownership: they were thus aping their betters and must be put in their places.

It now seems almost incredible that snobbery of this kind existed; but exist it did, and its influence upon the acceptance of the motor vehicle should not be underestimated. In particular it affected relations between motorists and the police. In a great many districts, particularly in the south of England, the magisterial benches were almost exclusively occupied by the minor landowning or retired-officer classes, who were particularly class conscious and who were generally rabid horse-lovers of the kind who could not see that mechanization would free their favourite animals from conditions of toil which grew steadily worse as traffic increased.

Magistrates of this sort, when confronted with a supposedly errant motorist, often accepted evidence which should have been laughed out of court, always imposed the maximum penalty the law allowed and usually accompanied their judgements with unwarranted jibes and insults. This magisterial prejudice naturally influenced the police, particularly over speeding offences; during the hey-day of the police 'traps' it was quite common for motor cars to be timed over the measured distance (usually a furlong, and usually on a piece of straight country road), by two constables who were not even furnished with stop watches. They were supposed to make do with ordinary watches—sometimes even without seconds hands—and as they had to hide behind hedges or trees they were often so far away from the limits of the measured distance that their judgement was affected by parallax. One famous police sergeant contrived to trap cars which he could not see as they entered and left his measured furlong; he worked single-handed (which was illegal and ultimately his undoing) by 'timing' the progress of the dust cloud from a church porch sufficiently far away from the measured stretch for him to be able to make his calculations and still have time to stroll into the road to stop the offending motorist. His zeal was matched by the anti-motoring activities of one Surrey J. P. which led him to take station in a coign of vantage near a low garden wall from which he could pelt passing motor cars with clods of garden refuse: this splendid keeper of the King's peace was the writer's great-uncle. The administration of the law towards the motorist fell into a state of disrepute from which it has never fully recovered.

The attitude of the police was also coloured by the belief that the automobile was a rich man's plaything. For the first time the 'nobs' were put in a position where they could be 'in trouble with the police', a state of affairs hitherto almost exclusively reserved for the lower orders. In Victorian and Edwardian England the upper and middle classes all too often exhibited to the police, as public servants, the kind of 'here-my-good-man' superiority they asserted over their private servants, and the police would have been less than human had they not resented this and, subconsciously perhaps, seized the opportunity which the motor car gave them to redress the balance.

Although the fallacy of the motorist being part of a wealthy minority still colours official thinking to some extent, the truth is that possession of a car never was exclusively reserved to the rich. It is true that many very wealthy men took up motoring as a sport or hobby in the early days, and spent prodigious sums (one thinks of the Duke of Portland with his six cars and twelve chauffeurs), but Carl Benz himself had visualized the petrol car as an alternative to the pony and trap rather than to the barouche and pair; a great many manufacturers thought as he did and catered accordingly. The figures speak for themselves; in 1901 the Marquis de Dion sold more than 1,500 of his little rear-engined single-cylinder voiturettes (a large proportion of them to the English), but between 1904 and 1906 only thirty-seven of the thirty-horsepower six-cylinder Rolls-Royces were made. These proportions are roughly constant for the whole of our period, and it is because the 'man of modest means', as the period phrase had it, could afford a little runabout—a Dennis or a De Dion, a Swift or a Sizaire, a Rover or a Renault—that despite all opposition the motor developed so quickly and transformed social and business life so completely.

It is not possible here to trace the process which transformed the snorting, palpitating, evil-smelling, underpowered and often unreliable horseless carriage of the 1890s into the quiet, swift, smooth-running elegant conveyance which the motor became, in its finest form, by the time King Edward VII died. By that time even the single- or twin-cylinder light cars, which were still somewhat rough and noisy by modern standards, gave their owners reliable transportation at less than pony-and-trap costs. Motor bicycles, tri-cars and the 'cycle cars' which were just coming into fashion, though stark and often crude in design and execution, brought motoring of a kind almost down to working-class level. The mechanical developments can best be summed up by saying that the specific output of Benz's first tri-car engine was slightly less than 1 h.p. per litre; by the end of the nineteenth century typical car engines, such as Panhard-Levassor and Daimler, gave about $3\frac{1}{2}$ h.p. per litre, though the remarkable little 'high-speed' De Dion Bouton 'singles' had achieved 7 h.p. per litre by 1896. By 1908 some racing units reached an output of just over 10 h.p. per litre, though the average was only about seven: there were wide variations; the 40/50 Rolls-Royce, for example, developing 48 h.p. at 1,750 r.p.m. from slightly more than 7 litres against the 'Twenty-eight' Lanchester's 42 h.p. at 2,200 r.p.m. from 3.8 litres. By 1914 the extreme of efficiency was represented by the Grand Prix Sunbeam at 30 h.p. per litre.

It is not easy to assess costs in present-day terms, as the structure of social life has changed as completely as monetary values. During the whole period under review it was possible to buy a new motor car (of the simplest single- or twin-cylinder two-seater variety usually) for £150; for the man content with a tri-car, quadricycle or cycle-car as little as £85 might suffice. At the other end of the scale the common practice of pricing the larger cars for the bare chassis exclusive of bodywork, supplied and fitted by an 'outside' coach-builder, lamps and other accessories, complicates the assessment. Lanchester was the first English manufacturer to insist on designing the car as an entity and making his own coachwork; his company offered their five-seater 12 h.p. model in 1903, complete with all fitments, special tools, expendable spares and tyres, for £550, but the nearest comparable model of Daimler cost £700 for the bare chassis. In 1905 the 30 h.p. six-cylinder Rolls-Royce was priced at £890 for the chassis and the comparable Napier was £1,050. The Silver Ghost Rolls-Royce chassis was excellent value at £850, and by 1914 the excellent four-cylinder Morris-Oxford was offered at £175 complete with body-work and all accessories. This was probably the cheapest English four-cylinder car on the market, but the ubiquitous Model T Ford at £125 was quickly becoming dominant in the 'cheap car' field.

Running costs are also difficult to compute, but tyres were un-deniably the most expensive item at first. The pioneer motorist of the cartoon or musical-hall joke was depicted as a begoggled monster who spent rare moments of ecstatic motion, scattering hens, dogs, children and old women in terror before his dust cloud, and weary hours stranded by the roadside struggling with recalcitrant and in-comprehensible machinery. Some of the first machines, admittedly, were badly designed and unreliable, but most of these roadside break-downs were occasioned by punctured or burst tyres. The pioneer motorists' ignorance of machinery accounted for much of the trouble, and some simple mishap like a discharged battery, a faulty electrical connection or a carburettor jet choked with road dust would result in an ignominious tow home behind a 'hay motor' and urgent tele-grams asking the manufacturer to send a man to repair the fault. Tyre failures, however, haunted novice and expert alike and, by some quirk, the simple solution of making rims or wheels detachable and interchangeable so that a spare could be carried was not found until surprisingly late. The business of repairing a puncture (or putting on a new, stiff, spare cover to replace a burst), with the wheel *in situ* usually took at least half an hour, and in the first years a journey of 100 miles without a puncture was something to write home about.

The tyres improved quickly, but, for some years, not quickly enough to keep pace with improved car performance. In 1902 a small light car, very carefully driven at not more than 25 m.p.h., might (with luck) cover 2,000 miles before its expensive tyres were worn out; but some large, heavy fast vehicle—say a Napier 'Sixty'—might well destroy its covers in 700 miles or so. There were wide differences in tyre consumption between one make of car and another even though weights and performances were apparently similar, and this brought home to manufacturers the need to study suspension design and the importance of reducing unsprung weight. In 1907 a 40 h.p. Siddeley was subjected to a long-distance test under the observation of the Royal Automobile Club during which it consumed tyres at the appalling rate of one every 631 miles; a few weeks later the Club supervised the Rolls-Royce 40/50 on its famous 15,000 miles test and found that it only required one tyre for every 2,500 miles. The total distance covered was considered equal to three years' average use, and taking tyres and all other expenses into account the R.A.C. calculated that the Rolls-Royce cost fourpence halfpenny a mile. This was remarkably cheap but impecunious motorists, content with small light cars and able to do their own repairs, could motor for as little as twopence a mile.

Fuel costs were always a relatively minor item; petrol was untaxed until 1909, when an impost of threepence a gallon was added to the basic price, which was between 1s. and 1s. 6d. The most expensive form of motoring was by means of the battery-electric broughams and landaulets which were fashionable for town work. They were usually run on annual contract-hire with the supplier responsible for battery charging and maintenance. The cost to the hirer (including driver's wages) was not far short of 2s. 6d. a mile on the average usage of thirty miles a day for 300 days in the year; but this was considerably less than the cost of keeping a carriage, two horses, coachman and stable boy.

The Act of 1903 which raised the speed limit to 20 m.p.h. made registration and the display of identification marks compulsory. It is difficult to estimate the number of motor vehicles in use before then, but it is probably safe to say that there were fewer than 1,000 mechanical vehicles of all kinds in Great Britain at the time of the 1,000 Miles Trial in 1900. The Treasury returns (covering England and Wales only) for 1911–12 show that licence duty was paid on:

Cabs and omnibuses	31,260
Other motor vehicles	144,328
TOTAL	175,588

New vehicles first registered in 1913–14 amounted to 26,238 and it is estimated that there were a quarter of a million mechanical vehicles of all types on the roads of Great Britain at the outbreak of the 1914 war; of these 130,000 were private cars or cycles.

The social revolution worked by the mechanization of goods and public passenger road carriers, though far less glamorous and consequently less well recorded than the changes wrought by the private motor car, is probably of greater significance than any other effect of the industrial revolution. The effect has been on balance beneficial: no matter how much we, as individuals, may curse the pebble-scattering, hustling, gravel merchant's lorry as it is blatantly driven across our bows at twenty or more miles an hour above its supposed maximum pace, ignored by the police who pounce upon us if we exceed our limit by a tenth of the amount; or groan as we join the long queue of traffic creeping behind some extraordinary load drawn by a smoke-belching diesel monster which none dare pass because of the inadequacy of the road, we know that the structure of our society would collapse if they were not there. Repeated strikes have shown that it is possible to carry on, at great inconvenience and expense, without the railways, but the consequences of a total cessation of all road traffic would bring chaos. A man who suffers a blocked artery may live as the venous circulation takes over whilst the blockage is removed, but a total venous stoppage brings gangrene and death. The proposal made by the Minister of Transport, just before these lines were written, deliberately to restrict venous circulation by discriminatory taxation and special imposts is as mischievous a piece of nonsense as any to have been put before Parliament since Colonel Charles de Laet Sibthorpe advocated limiting railway speeds to six miles an hour on the grounds that the draught made by a faster pace would so act upon the locomotive's furnace as to invite explosion and death.

The heavy traction engines remained in production, almost unchanged, into the 1920s, and many of them were still at work in the 'thirties, but lighter and handier steam goods carriers were seen on the roads very soon after the 1896 Act took effect. Many of the firms who made them are still in business and some had their roots in the first stage of the industrial revolution; but the first 'modern' steam lorry to be sold was a tipping dustcart made for the Chiswick Council by Thornycroft and Co., whose experience of steam-engineering only goes back to 1864, when they began making their famous steam launches.

The first experimental Thornycroft steam van antedated the dustcart by a year and clearly showed its maritime parentage in its water-tube boiler and launch engine. It had the peculiarity of driving on its front wheels and steering by the hinder ones, and also has the alleged distinction of having conveyed Queen Victoria's washing to and from Windsor Castle. This picturesque fable can only be believed by those who can also believe that the royal smalls were entrusted to some local bagwash; but this steam van, which is still in running order, was the first of a distinguished line.

In 1898 a Thornycroft four-ton lorry carried off the first prize at the Liverpool Self-Propelled Traffic Association's trials, and in 1900 the firm earned Lord Kitchener's praise when he wrote of the steamers used in South Africa during the Boer War: 'The motor lorries . . . did very well; Thornycrofts are the best.' Before the end of the nineteenth century Thornycroft had introduced an articulated six-wheeler and their rigid lorries were fitted with Weston multi-disc clutches to facilitate gear-changing whilst in motion (many of their rivals, like the old traction engines, had to stop to change from normal to emergency low gear). They also had enclosed high-speed under-floor engines and self-feeding furnaces. The Thornycroft three-ton-tare steamer could carry four tons on the platform and draw another three on a trailer. In 1903 the firm began to make petrol-engined lorries and private cars.

Steam lorries developed along two main lines; the 'undertype' of which the Thornycroft was the first example in Great Britain and which culminated in the splendid Sentinel rigid four-axle eight-tonner of 1933, and the 'overtype' which evolved out of the traction engine. Foden is the name chiefly associated with the 'overtype', and despite the reduction in platform space (if the wheelbase was to be kept within reasonable bounds) occasioned by the length of the locomotive boiler, the type was well liked for its simplicity and durability. Putting the engine on top of the boiler, traction-engine fashion, minimized heat losses, kept the motion work under the driver's eye and simplified lubrication and maintenance. Until almost the end of its long career the 'overtype' lorry retained the old-fashioned centre-pivoted steering axle, and a peculiarity of many of the Fodens was that the driver sat on a saddle astride the near-side engine framing, so that his right foot gently frizzled beside the fire door and his left foot froze on its exposed stirrup. The last 'undertype' steamers, like the Sentinel, were capable of 50 m.p.h., but the older-fashioned 'overtypes' were only capable of about twelve m.p.h., except for some of the last to be made, which were mounted on pneumatic tyres and geared to run at twenty m.p.h. Like the traction engines on which they were based, they were virtually indestructible and some of them saw more than forty years' continuous service. The standard pattern Foden 'overtype' could carry six tons on the platform and draw another four on a trailer at 10 m.p.h. for a coal consumption of about one hundredweight every twenty miles.

It is not possible to mention all the many manufacturers who made steam lorries, but amongst those who have survived the Leyland concern should not be ignored. The business started in the smithy of the village of Leyland in Lancashire early in the nineteenth century and continued as a thriving family concern, with ramifications into agricultural engineering, until it came into the hands of James Sumner in 1892. As a young man Sumner had made a steam tricycle and followed it with a five-ton capacity wagon in 1884; this was not very satisfactory, but after buying the Leyland business Sumner produced two more steam tri-cars, which he sold, and then started a regular line of steam lawn mowers. His growing business attracted the brothers George and Henry Spurrier who joined him, bringing in more capital, practical experience of railway-locomotive design and useful connections with the Stott and Coulthard engineering firms.

Plans were laid to produce steam lorries before the 1896 Act went through and the first of these were on sale in 1897; they had some features in common with the Coulthard steam vans, which did not stay in production long. The Lancashire Steam Motor Co., as the Leyland business was then called, had an oil-burning four-ton capacity lorry in production by 1898, and other pioneers in the use of liquid fuel were Clarkson & Capel (whose steam buses were widely used), Lifu the (Liquid Fuel Company) of the Isle of Wight, and Simpson and Bodman, whose high-pressure boiler and three-cylinder radial high-speed engine were of most advanced design. In general, though, the British buyers of steam lorries preferred solid fuel, as its disadvantages were outweighed by its cheapness.

Leyland made their last steam lorry in 1926 and their first petrol lorry, known as *The Pig*, in 1904. It was the first of a very distinguished line, and the company made their first double-deck bus for the L.G.O.C. in the following year. Until the London General and Vanguard companies set up their own manufacturing depart-

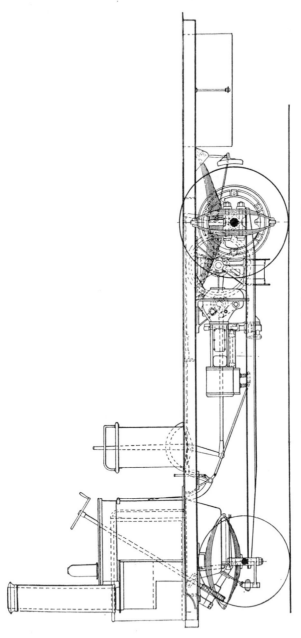

Figure 15 Thornycroft Steam Lorry 1898

ment Leyland's were the principal suppliers of London bus chassis, and the famous L.G.O.C. 'B' Type had much in common with the Leyland 'subsidy' three-tonner, of which over 5,000 were supplied to the Forces during the war.

Although generalizations are always fair game for those who enjoy proving writers inaccurate, it is probably safe to say that for a variety of technical and constructional reasons the internal-combustion lorry could not compete with the steam lorry for payloads much above five tons before 1914. During the war great numbers of petrol lorries were impressed or manufactured for war service, but steam (and petrol-electric) lorries were not taken and steam therefore kept its dominant place in heavy civilian haulage work during the war. When thousands of ex-service lorries, mostly of the W.D. three-ton specification, were sold into civilian service in 1919–20 a gap was still there for steam to fill. The pre-war bias towards steam for heavy work was disappearing, but the advantage of cheap home-produced fuel helped the steamer to hold its own for a few more years. It was under heavy pressure from new designs of heavy-load petrol lorries towards the end of the 1920s and had to bow to the diesel engine in the early 'thirties. The road steamer, as we have seen, reached its apogee with the last *Sentinel* design of 1933: these splendid machines were last made in 1936, or one hundred years after Hancock had so nearly succeeded in putting steam to regular work on London's streets.

Although some types were inevitably less successful than others, the steam lorry was a reliable, and therefore commercially acceptable, vehicle from its inception. The same cannot be said of the first petrol-engined goods vehicles. One of the participants in Lawson's farcical Emancipation Day London to Brighton Run was a Daimler 'breakdown van' laden with tools and spares which earned unenviable fame for the variety of perverse and ingenious ways in which it broke down on the short journey, and rather similar unreliability characterized other early attempts to harness the newfangled 'motor' for delivery work. One of the reasons for this was that most early goods vehicles were made by putting a van or truck body on some existing car chassis, which was then found too light and too underpowered for the job.

The breakdowns and expense occasioned by tyre failures also delayed the commercial success of the petrol motor goods vehicle. It is true that all but a few of the first steam lorries also ran on solid rubber tyres, which were expensive and, at first, unreliable, but as their permitted speeds were less their tyre failures were proportionately fewer than those suffered by the lighter and faster newcomers. Inexperience both on the manufacturing and operating sides led to a lot of avoidable mechanical failures, which were not suffered with the steam lorries as they had more than a century of knowledge, however apparently remote, behind them.

As we have seen (Chapter 5), the first operators of relatively small motor buses found themselves faced with tyre costs of tenpence a mile or more, and also suffered severely from transmission failures brought about by the combination of inflexible engines and inexpert drivers. It was not until the middle 'twenties that the pneumatic tyre was developed to a point where it was capable of carrying the heavier vehicles. Until then omnibuses and goods carriers of two tons or more payload almost invariably ran on solids. The teething troubles with these were largely overcome by about 1905, and the solid rubber tyre thereafter became quite reliable and economical for loads up to ten tons per axle and speeds up to about 25 m.p.h. The design and construction of the heavier petrol lorries were necessarily influenced by the need to make them massive enough to stand the hammering of solid tyres on rough roads—and any reader old enough to remember riding on a wooden-seated, solid-tyred motor bus over stone setts will understand why some of the first motor vehicles shook and rattled themselves into an early grave.

It is doubtful whether any tradesman or carrier who tried to work with petrol vehicles before 1900 was able to bring the costs below those of horse traction. Between 1900 and 1905 the lighter commercial vehicles, for payloads of a ton or less, succeeded in establishing themselves, and the breakthrough point for heavier carriers came between 1905 and 1908, during which time down-to-earth carriers such as Pickfords found it commercially profitable to begin replacing their horses and steamers with motors. By 1909 the petrol lorry of two to four tons capacity was firmly established, not only as a reliable performer able in time to price the horse out of business but also of extraordinary durability. Annual mileages expected of a goods vehicle were, it is true, less then than now, but planned obsolescence was not a quality which would have appealed to the businessman of sixty years ago and the carrier who bought a motor lorry before the Great War expected it to give him at least ten years' service. Many gave much more: large numbers of the 'subsidy' or impressed lorries, together with those specially built, returned to civilian use after four years of struggling through Flanders mud. They were then mostly modernized by the addition of enclosed driving cabs, electric lights and, ultimately, pneumatic tyres and a number of them were still profitably at work in the 'thirties. It was no uncommon thing to find a lorry designed for a three-ton payload at 20 m.p.h. carrying five tons or more on the platform, hauling another two or more in a trailer and taking advantage of its pneumatic tyres to push along at 30 m.p.h. with no apparent loss of reliability. Few manufactured products have improved so dramatically as the petrol motor lorry did between 1900 and 1914.

Alterations to the tare-load ratio, to speed limits and to other details which were made by the Acts of 1903 and 1909 suffered the usual defects of being too cautious and not taking account of probable technical progress. The 1896 Act had allowed only 5 m.p.h. for vehicles above two tons tare, and by the end of our period this had risen to 12 m.p.h. for lorries without trailers. Both these limits, and the slightly more generous speeds allowed to the lighter goods vehicles, were lower than was necessary in relation to the technical developments of the time and they were consequently held in contempt. The private motorist was severely, and often unjustly, punished if he went over his permitted 12 m.p.h. or 20 m.p.h. limits, but the police were apparently reluctant to act against commercial drivers and operators whose running schedules had to be based on illegal speeds if they were to pay their way. The driver of 1898, supposedly limited to 5 m.p.h., habitually drove at 8 m.p.h. where gradients and traffic permitted, just as his modern counterpart who is theoretically limited to 40 m.p.h. (except on the motorways) habitually drives at 65 m.p.h. wherever he has a chance of doing so.

There are three possible reasons why the police, then and now, appeared less ready to prosecute the 'commercial' than the 'private' law-breaker. Firstly, because of a 'brothers under the skin' feeling of class affinity with the one and class hostility against the other: secondly because of their own common-sense recognition 'that the law is a h'ass and lastly that the problem is just beyond them. Unfortunately the result has been to heighten antagonism between private motorists and police, and to make a privileged class to the extent where the speed-loving young enthusiast will soon be tempted to buy a ten-ton lorry rather than a sports car.

In other areas where legislation *was* needed to protect the public nothing was done. It was not until 1919 that insurance against third-party claims was made compulsory, and this should have been done much sooner. Most private motorists insured in their own interests, but the majority of commercial operators did not and this often inflicted hardship on those least able to bear it. Between 1904, when two people died, and the end of 1912, 478 fatal injuries were inflicted by London's motor buses, but fewer than a dozen of the victims' families were compensated. Those who were compensated were of the class accustomed to dealing with lawyers and paying their fees, but it is only fair to the motor buses to add that these fatalities were proportionately no greater than those suffered by the victims of horse-bus accidents.

The Road Board created by the Act of 1909 (9 Edw. VII, c. 47) was not empowered to devote any of the money raised by the new vehicle duties and fuel tax to ordinary road maintenance (see Chapter 4), and this gave rise to a genuine grievance which, in part, persists to this day. The local authorities and their ratepayers felt aggrieved that their roads were being worn out by the new traffic whilst they were not entitled to any of the new income (nearly £1,000,000 was collected in the first full year), and all road-users felt, and still feel, cheated over the inadequacy of the improvements and the lack of new trunk roads which were so urgently needed.

The new motor vehicles only gradually added to the traffic jams which had been a feature of the scene in London and many provincial towns for more than a century. Indeed, it is possible that the coming of the motor reduced congestion for a time by providing smaller and handier substitutes for certain numbers of horsed vehicles. Inevitably, though, the total traffic increased, the blockages grew worse and the inadequacy of the 'main' roads became more and more obvious as through traffic reappeared on them after three-quarters of a century.

Experts of all kinds, from highway engineers, local government officials and motorist journalists of the calibre of the second Lord Montagu of Beaulieu stressed the urgency of the problem in the first years of the century; but nothing was done to make new roads, though the surface improvements on the existing roads were dramatic and commendable.

The pressure continued after the Great War and the first few hesitant steps towards making 'arterial' roads were taken after the effects of four years' neglect had been made good. The merits of motorways, from which horses and pedestrians should be excluded, and with bridges or tunnels to take crossing traffic, were admirably argued in 1924 by Hilaire Belloc, who took as his example an imaginary London–Birmingham motorway which, as he described it, exactly foreshadowed in its route, its width, its curves, its gradients and its crossings, the actual road which was constructed a generation after he had pointed out how badly it was needed. The delay seems depressingly familiar.

Like Beaumont before him, and many since, Belloc[2] wrote of the folly of complicating legislation by too much attention to technical details. Of taxation he wrote:

> . . . in so far as you tax travel for the purposes of this [road building] fund you should tax it not by any complicated combination of weight, power, fuel and so forth, but through some one factor, otherwise you will be perpetually remodelling your scheme and as perpetually causing a grievance . . . If you want to have easy revenue simplicity in taxation is essential . . . So long as a false distinction is maintained between the private and the commercial use of vehicles you will have gross anomalies and injustices . . .

We now seem to be about to witness the rebirth of discriminatory taxation, and legislation deliberately designed to drive traffic off the roads. In a country as small and as hideously overpopulated as this the Minister of Transport has a particularly difficult job, and is bound to offend someone, but the present Minister and his advisers and successors should be invited to ponder the words those great Socialists, Sidney and Beatrice Webb, wrote fifty-five years ago:

> . . . history lends no support to the idea that we can, merely to save ourselves the cost of reconstructing the roads, advantageously set a limit to the size, or the weight, or the character of the vehicles that lawfully use the King's Highway . . . It is difficult to estimate boldly enough the increase in wealth production, the reduction in the cost of living, and the growth of freedom and amenity that would be promoted by further improvements in road locomotion.

Taxes and Toll Charges

The rates of taxation on vehicles have been changed so many times since a tax was first imposed three hundred years ago that it is not possible to give full details in the space available. The following notes give a general indication.

In 1790 the annual duty on four-wheeled carriages was £8 16s. 0d. for the first, £9 18s. 0d. for the second and £11 for each one above that number. The duty on two-wheeled carriages was £3 7s. 0d. unless they cost less than £12 and displayed the legend 'Taxed Cart' painted on in large letters, whereupon the tax was only 12s. The limitation on cost meant, generally, that the 'Taxed Carts', which included most of the gigs used by farmers and tradesmen, were unsprung.

Postmasters keeping one horse and one post-chaise were taxed £7 10s. 0d. p.a., rising to £60 p.a. on the maximum permitted number of twenty horses and fifteen carriages. Horses only, let on hire without carriages, were taxed at 7s. 6d. p.a. plus 1½d. for every mile travelled. This represents a tax of 4s. on every £1 earned by each horse.

Stage-coaches, in addition to having to display licence plates for which an annual fee was payable to the Stamp Office, were also taxed at 1½d. a mile from 1799 to 1825. In 1845–6 the minimum tax payable on a four-wheeled carriage was £6 rising to £9 1s. 6d. for each carriage kept above a total of nine. This bore heavily on 'job masters', whose contract-hire carriages were taxed at 'private' rates.

In 1854 the scale of tax on stage-coach (i.e. by then, omnibus) mileage and on post-horses was reduced, the private carriage tax for four-wheelers was reduced to £3 10s. 0d. and Gladstone in 1869 made further reductions to £2 0s. 0d. on four-wheelers and 15s. on two-wheelers. These reductions brought a great increase in the use

225

of carriages and of two-wheelers used, for example, for delivery work by butchers and other shopkeepers; revenue also rose. With minor adjustments this scale of tax remained in force until the end of the century, and the first private motor cars were taxed as four-wheel carriages.

Toll charges varied widely throughout the period; they also differed greatly between one trust and another and were subject to frequent changes by the individual trusts in response to local pressures. Certain types of traffic, coal for example, would be exempt in one year and charged in the next. Agricultural traffic was generally exempt for produce and livestock being taken or driven to market. Vehicles taking people to church or to county elections were frequently exempted, but many trusts charged double toll on Sunday travellers and some put a surcharge of 50 per cent on all tolls between 31 October and 1 May.

Where the roads were 'piked' travellers on wheels and driven animals were, in effect, taxed every seven miles on average. In 1774 Parson Woodforde recorded that a post-chaise journey for two people from Bath to Oxford—hire, mileage duty, tolls and meals—cost £15 8s. 0d. or half the average annual income of a curate.

The following scale of tolls charged by the Bruton Trust in Somerset at their Batcomb gate is representative of the costs in the first quarter of the nineteenth century. It can be calculated that the tolls for a four-horse coach or carriage represent a surcharge of approximately $2\frac{1}{4}d.$ a mile, which must be set against the background of a wage of tenpence to one shilling a day for a labourer.

For every Horse or Mule, drawing any Coach, Barouche, Sociable, Chariot, Landau, Chaise, Phaeton, Curricle, Gig, Cart upon Springs, Hearse, Litter or other like Carriage	$4\frac{1}{2}d.$
For every such carriage, on more than two wheels, being empty drawn at the tail of any other carriage	$3d.$
For every such carriage on two wheels only, empty and so drawn	$1\frac{1}{2}d.$
For every horse or mule drawing any Waggon, Cart, Caravan or other such carriage, having the fellies of the wheels of less breadth than four and a half inches	$6d.$
Ditto of the breadth of four and a half inches and less than six inches	$5d.$
Ditto of six inches and less than nine inches	$4d.$
Ditto, nine inches and upward	$3d.$

(The toll of two Oxen or Neat Cattle drawing to be equal to that of one Horse)

For every Ass drawing any Waggon, Cart or other Carriage	4*d*.
For every Horse or Mule not drawing	1½*d*.
For every Ass not drawing	1*d*.
For Oxen, Cows, or Neat Cattle, each	½*d*.
For Hogs, Calves, Sheep or Lambs, each	¼*d*.

Source References

CHAPTER TWO

1 *Annals of Agriculture*, vol. 2, 1786.
2 J. T. Rutt (editor), *Diary of Thomas Burton*, London, 1828.
3 E. Littleton, *Proposal for Repairing and Maintaining the Highways*, British Museum Pamphlet, 1692.
4 John Scott, *Digest of the General Highway and Turnpike Laws*, 1778.
5 Idem.
6 Sidney and Beatrice Webb, *English Local Government*, vol. V, *The Story of the King's Highway*, Cambridge, 1913.
7 Sir John Hawkins, *Observations on the state of the Highways*, 1763.
8 Sidney and Beatrice Webb, op. cit.
9 Rev. Dr Richard Burn, *The Justice of the Peace*, vol. II, 1758.
10 L. T. C. Rolt, *Thomas Telford*, London, 1958.

CHAPTER THREE

1 *Journal*, Royal Statistical Society, 1839: Report, Royal Commission on Roads, 1840.
2 Craik and Macfarlane, *Pictorial History of England*, 1855, and R. D. G. Price, 'Rebeccaism', in *Nineteenth Century Magazine*, 1888.
3 Sir George Cornwall Lewis, *Letters*, London, 1870.
4 Charles Penfold, *A Practical Treatise on the Best Modes of Making Roads*, London, 1835, and Hobhouse, *An Outline of Local Government and Local Taxation*, London, 1884.
5 Sidney and Beatrice Webb, op. cit.
6 Sir George Cornwall Lewis, op. cit.

CHAPTER FOUR

1 John Loudon McAdam, *Remarks on the Present System of Road-making*, Bristol, 1818.

2 John Scott, *Digests of the General Highway and Turnpike Laws*, 1778.

3 R. L. Edgeworth, *An Essay on the Construction of Roads and Carriages*, 1813.

4 13 Geo. III, c. 84, s. 4.

5 Thomas De Quincey, *Autobiographic Sketches*, 1803.

6 Sir Henry Parnell, *A Treatise on Roads*, London, 1838.

7 Anonymous, *The Roads and Railroads, Vehicles and Modes of Travelling of Ancient and Modern Countries*, British Museum Pamphlet, 1839.

8 Local Taxation Returns.

CHAPTER FIVE

1 Joseph Storrs Fry, *An Essay on the Construction of Wheel Carriages, etc.*, London, 1820.

2 James Reid, *The Evolution of Horse-Drawn Vehicles*, London, 1933.

3 William Bridges Adams, *English Pleasure Carriages*, London, 1837.

4 Idem.

5 Walter Hancock, *Narrative of Twelve Years Experiments . . . of Steam Carriages etc. etc.*, London, 1838.

CHAPTER SIX

1 James Felton, *Observations upon the Construction . . . of Wheel Carriages . . . with . . . Animadversions . . . upon Broad Wheels, etc.* London, 1790.

2 W. C. A. Blew, *Brighton and its Coaches*, London, 1894.

3 Henry Charles Moore, *Omnibuses and Cabs*, London, 1902.

4 James Reid, *The Evolution of Horse Drawn Carriages*, London, 1933.

5 George Athelstane Thrupp, *The History of Coaches*, London, 1877.

6 William Bridges Adams, *English Pleasure Carriages*, London, 1837.

7 Joseph Storrs Fry, *An Essay on the Construction of Wheel Carriages . . . etc.*, London, 1820.

8 R. L. Edgeworth, *An Account of Some Experiments Conducted on the Draught of Wheel Carriages, . . . etc.* Dublin, 1816.

9 Joseph Jacob, *Observations on the Structure and Draught of Wheel Carriages*, London, 1773.

10 William Bridges Adams, *English Pleasure Carriages*, London, 1837.

11 William Bridges Adams, op. cit.

CHAPTER SEVEN

1 Charles Dickens, *Posthumus Papers of the Pickwick Club*, 1836.

2 Nimrod, *pseud.* for C. J. Apperley, in *Sporting Magazine*, etc.

3 C. R. Clear, *John Palmer*, Blandford, 1935.

4 George Athelstane Thrupp, *A History of Coaches*, London, 1894.

5 W. C. A. Blew, *Brighton and its Coaches*, London, 1894.
See also Thomas De Quincey, *The English Mail Coach*, London, 1803, and Edmund Vale, *The Mail Coach Men of the Late Eighteenth Century*, London, 1900.

CHAPTER EIGHT

1 Henry Charles Moore, *Omnibuses and Cabs*, London, 1902.

2 James Reid, *The Evolution of Horse Drawn Carriages*, London, 1933.

3 George Athelstane Thrupp, *The History of Coaches*, London, 1877.

4 D. Farman, *Auto-Cars*, London, 1896.

5 E. L. Cornwell, *Commercial Road Vehicles*, London, 1960.
W. Worby Beaumont, *Motor Vehicles and Motors*, London, 1900.

6 Anthony Bird, *The Motor Car*, 1765–1914, London, 1960.

7 E. L. Cornwell, *Commercial Road Vehicles*, London, 1960.

8 Idem.

9 Sidney and Beatrice Webb, *History of Local Government*, vol. V, Cambridge, 1913.

10 London Passenger Transport Board Records.

CHAPTER NINE

1 Charles Dickens, *Sketches by Boz*, 1836.
2 H. C. Moore, *Omnibuses and Cabs*, London, 1902.
3 *London Magazine, Gentlemen's Magazine.*
4 Moore, op. cit.
5 W. Worby Beaumont, *Motor Vehicles and Motors*, London, 1900.

CHAPTER TEN

1 Walter Hancock, *A Narrative of Twelve Years Experiments etc. Demonstrative of . . . Steam Carriages . . .* London, 1838.
2 Samuel Smiles, *Lives of the Engineers*, London, 1881.
3 William Fletcher, *Steam Locomotion on Common Roads*, London, 1891.
4 Samuel Smiles, *Invention and Industry*, London 1884.
5 W. Worby Beaumont, *Motor Vehicles and Motors*, London, 1900.
6 Sir Goldsworthy Gurney, *Observations on Steam Carriages on Turnpike Roads etc. etc.*, London, 1832.
7 Col. Francis Maceroni, *Life*, London, 1843.
8 Anthony Bird, 'The Yellow Emperor's South-Pointing Chariot' in *Antiquarian Horology*, March 1961.

CHAPTER ELEVEN

1 Charles Dickens, *American Notes*, 1844.
2 David Scott-Moncrieff, *Veteran and Edwardian Motor Cars*, London, 1955.
3 W. Worby Beaumont, *Motor Vehicles and Motors*, London, 1900.
4 William Fletcher, *Steam Locomotion on Common Roads*, London, 1900.
5 Idem.

CHAPTER TWELVE

1 Anthony Bird and Francis Hutton-Scott, *Lanchester Motor Cars*, London, 1965.
2 Hilaire Belloc, *The Road*, London, 1924.

Gazetteer

No complete guide to the visible remains of parish and turnpike roads has yet been made. As the processes of straightening, widening and easing gradients (often by making a cut-off) have been almost unceasing for two centuries, the task of providing an accurate record would be prodigious. Nevertheless, individual workers and local preservation, record, and industrial archaeology societies have made valiant efforts in recent years to record and photograph surviving traces of vanished roads (often startlingly visible in aerial photographs) and such toll houses, turnpike gates and mile stones of the period as are still to be seen.

Mile 'stones' and posts (often of cast iron) are the only relics which are still plentiful, and the Holyhead road, for which Telford designed the mile-posts, as well as the road itself and all other appurtenances, still has some fine examples. Now that the traveller no longer has to rely on milestones to check the distance covered, and the amount charged, many authorities do not trouble to replace them when road repairs or alterations necessitate their removal.

Local public libraries and museums are the best starting-points for investigation of any given locality, and the 1817 Ordnance Survey, though not wholly accurate, gives the most complete picture available of the road system at, or near, the peak of the coaching age. Photostat copies of this first edition of the Survey may be seen in the Map room at the British Museum. Robin Atthill's *Old Mendip* (David & Charles, 1964) sheds light upon the fascination and magnitude of the sort of fieldwork needed, whilst also providing an example which others may be inspired to follow.

Vehicles may be examined at a variety of museums and trade or private collections. The emphasis is upon mechanical vehicles, particularly private cars, but there are good representative examples of horsed vehicles at the Science Museum (as well as excellent models, drawings and photographs), and at the Museum of Carriages in Maidstone.

The only known relics of the first steam-carriage era are at the Glasgow Museum, Kelvingrove, where an incomplete engine and some other remnants are on show which are, very probably, the remains of the Gurney Drag which was shipped to Leith in 1831. The only known survivor of the second period is the 1875 Grenville Steam Carriage which is preserved in running order at the Bristol City Museum.

Various private or semi-private collections of motor cars are open to the public by arrangement, but as the exhibits and arrangements vary from time to time they are excluded from the following list. Up-to-date information may be had from the Veteran Car Club of Great Britain, 14 Fitzhardinge Street, London W.1. Similarly some traction engines and early commercial vehicles are preserved in private ownership, and a number have been retained or bought back by their makers. The Historic Commercial Vehicle Club is the body responsible for recording such exhibits.

PUBLIC MUSEUMS

(Collections of fewer than six items excluded unless of special interest)

Birmingham City Museum and Art Gallery. Private cars, including loan items which are subject to variation, cycles, motor cycles, etc.

Bristol. The City Museum. The Granville Steam Carriage of 1875 and a small number of pre-1914 private cars.

British Transport Commission, Transport Museum, Clapham. * Various public-service passenger vehicles, horsed and horseless, including L.G.O.C. 'B' Type motor omnibus. Some commercial vehicles.

Coventry, City of Coventry Libraries and Museum, New Transport Gallery. Private cars, 1896 onwards, engines, accessories, some cycles, small number of carriages.

Edinburgh, The Royal Scottish Museum. A very small collection which includes the second car made the by Albion Company.

Glasgow Art Gallery and Museum. Parts of early steam carriage, believed to be Gurney and pre-1914 motor cars, etc., including

---

* At the time of writing plans have been announced to include this collection in the display at the York Railway Museum now under construction.

examples of Scottish manufacture—Argyll and Arroll-Johnston.

Hull (Kingston upon Hull) Municipal Museum. Private cars, including steam and electric, and some cycles, etc.

Maidstone Museum of Carriages. Horsed vehicles, trade and private, and appurtenances.

South Kensington Science Museum, Transport Gallery. Horsed and horseless vehicles from mid-eighteenth century to present day. Many interesting specimens are in the reserve collection, which can be seen by arrangement with the Keeper of the Land Transport Section. Models, drawings, parts and accessories are on view. The Museum has a particularly good collection of early bicycles, tricycles, etc., which is not on display at present, but which can be seen by arrangement. Noteworthy items are the mail-coach of 1827, Lord Brougham's brougham, Lanchester's Gold Medal phaeton and an 1888 model Benz which is almost certainly the oldest 'production model' petrol car in existence.

Victoria, S.W.1. The Royal Mews, Buckingham Palace Road. Guided tours, by arrangement only. The royal collection includes the State Coach of 1761 and relatively modern broughams, landaus and luggage brakes which are still in daily use.

The Montagu Motor Museum, Palace House, Beaulieu, Hampshire. A commercial concern providing refreshment and other facilities apart from the Museum. The collection is large, somewhat crowded and well documented. Private cars form the bulk of the collection, exhibits vary, there are some commercial vehicles, motor cycles and a very fine collection of early pedal cycles.

The Montagu Motor Museum, Brighton. Housed in the Aquarium buildings, an off-shoot of the Beaulieu Museum, private cars.

The Shuttleworth Memorial Trust, Old Warden Park, Biggleswade. The Shuttleworth collection includes a few horsed and many horseless carriages, cycles, farm tractors and aeroplanes, etc.

Select Bibliography

Aldin, Cecil Charles W., *The Romance of the Road*, London, 1933.

Anon., *The Roads and Railroads, Vehicles and Modes of Travelling in Great Britain, etc.*, London, 1839.

Ashworth, Robert, *Highway Engineering*, London, 1966.

Barker, Theodore, and Robbins, R. M. *A History of London Transport*, London, 1963.

Beazley, Elizabeth, *Design and Detail of the Spaces between Buildings*, London, 1960.

Bovill, Edward William, *The England of Nimrod and Surtees*, London, 1959.

Bradfield, John Edwin, *The Public Carriages of Great Britain*, London, 1855.

British Road Federation, *Basic Road Statistics*, Contemp.

Buchanan, C. D., *Mixed Blessing : the Motor Car in Britain*, London, 1958.

Burke, Thomas, *Travel in England*, London, 1952.

Cary, John, *Travellers Companion*, (many editions) London 1800 et. seq.

Clapham, J. H., *An Economic History of Great Britain*, Cambridge, 1939.

Cornwell, E. L., *Commercial Road Vehicles*, London, 1960.

Cumming, Alexander, *Observations of the Effects which Carriage Wheels have upon the Roads, etc.* London, 1797.

Deacon, William, *Remarks on Conical and Cylindrical Wheels, Public Roads, etc.*, London, 1808.

Durham, University of, *Urban Survival and Traffic* (*Proceedings of a symposium*), Durham, 1961.

Encyclopaedia of Highway Law and Practice (current—new volumes added as necessary), London,

Farman, D., *Auto-Cars*, London, 1896.

Fenton, B. W., *Municipal Engineering; Organization and Administration*, London, 1967.

Fordham, Sir Herbert George. *The Road Books and Itineraries of Great Britain from 1570 to 1850*, Cambridge, 1924.

Gardner, Leslie, *Stage Coach to John o'Groats*, London, 1961.

Gilbey, Sir Walter, *Modern Carriages*, London, 1905.

Goss, Anthony, *British Industry and Town Planning*, London, 1962.

Gregg, Pauline, *A Social and Economic History of Britain*, London, 1950.

Harper, Charles G., *The Dover Road, The Portsmouth Road etc.*, 15 vol., London, 1895.

Hay's Wharf Cartage Co., *Transport Saga 1646–1947* (Published by the Company), 1947.

Highway Engineering, Journal of the Institution of: *Article on Highways Organization*, June 1967.

Highway Engineers' Reference Book, Newnes, 1947.

Howard, Ebenezer, *Garden Cities of To-morrow* (1902, Revised 1946), London, 1946.

Hyde, James Wilson, *The Royal Mail*, Edinburgh, 1855.

Jacob, Joseph, *Animadversions on the Use of Broad Wheels, etc.*, London, 1773.

Karslake, Kent, and Pomeroy, Lawrence, *From Veteran to Vintage*, London, 1956.

Kent County Council, *Some Roads and Bridges: a collection of documents covering 16th to 19th Century* (Edited by Elizabeth Mellings) Kent Archives Office, 1959.

Leigh, Samuel (publisher), *Leigh's New Pocket Road Book of England and Wales*, London, 1837.

Margetson, Stella, *Journey by Stages*, London, 1967.

Mogg, Edward, *Survey of the High Roads of England and Wales*, London, 1817.

Oke, George Colwell, *The Law of Turnpike Roads*, London, 1861.

Oliver, George, *History of Coach Building*, London, 1962.

Pudney, James, *The Golden Age of Steam*, London, 1963.

Robertson, Alan W., *Great Britain's Post Roads, Post Towns and Postal Rates, 1635–1839*, London, 1961.

Robertson, Cecil, *Coachbuilding Past and Present*, London, 1928.

Robinson, Howard, *The British Post Office*, Princeton, 1948.

Rolt, L. T. C., *A Picture History of Motoring*, London, 1956.

Rolt, L. T. C., *Thomas Telford*, London, 1958.

Schreiber, Hermann, trans. Stewart Thompson, *The History of Roads*, London, 1961.

Science Museum, *History and Development of Cycles*, H.M.S.O., 1958.

Searle, Mark, *Turnpikes and Toll Bars*, London, 1930.

Selway, Neville Carr, *The Regency Road: the Coaching Prints of James Pollard*, London, 1957.

Tetlow, John, and Goss, Anthony, *Homes, Towns and Traffic*, London, 1965.

Tilling, John, *Kings of the Highway*, London, 1952.

Transport, Ministry of, *Concrete Road Construction*, H.M.S.O., 1964.

Trevithick, Francis, *Life of Richard Trevithick with an Account of his Inventions*, London, 1872.

Trussler, David J., *Early Buses and Trams*, London, 1964.

Unwin, A. C. B., *The Isleworth, Twickenham and Teddington Turnpikes 1762–1872* (Borough of Twickenham Local History Society), 1960.

Index

Abercromby, 58
Ackermann steering, 102–3, 150, 170
Adams, William Bridges, 79, 100, 102, 103
agricultural engine, *see* portable engine
Allen, Ralph, 113
Anderson, Sir James, 186, 190
Anglesey, Marquess of, 145
Anstruther, Colonel, 51
Anti-Dust Trials of 1908, 60
Argyll, Belsize, and Humber, 152
Argyll, Duke of, 51
Associated Equipment Company, 140
Austin Company, 104
Austin, Herbert, 208
Automobile Association, 64
Automobile Club, 43, 65
Aveling and Porter, 197

Barker and Company, 94
barouche, 87, 94, 107, 212, 226
Baudry, Monsieur, 127
Beale, 188, 189
Beaufoy, Henry, 51
Beaulieu, Lord Montagu of, 65
Beaulieu, second Lord Montagu of, 223, 224
Beaumont, W. Worby, 165, 205
Beeston Motor Tricycle, 207
Belloc, Hilaire, 224
Belsize, 152
Benson Driving Club, 112

Benz motor car, 41, 202, 203, 208, 209, 212, 213
Berliet car, 210
berlin, 87, 96
Bersey, Walter, 149, 150, 207
Besant, John, 77
and Patent Improved Wheel Carriage, 117, 118–20
Besant & Vidler, 118
bicycle, 40, 41–2, 59, 63, 79, 82, 84, 86, 206, 207, 208, 211
motor bicycle, 213, 215
Bill for Repairing of the Highways and Improving the Public Roads, 15
'Bills of Mortality', 145
Birch, J. Manley, 134
Blenkinsop, 165
Blunt, Colonel, 91
Bollée, Amédée, 190, 202
Bonner, Charles, 116, 117, 118, 124
boonmaster, *see* surveyor of highways
Boulton, Matthew, 119, 160
Boydell, 165
Bradshaw, 145
brakes, 87, 112
shooting-brake, 112
luggage-brake, 112
Bramah, Joseph, 168
Bramble, Matthew, 5
Brindley, 5
British Fisheries Society, 51
British Motor Syndicate Ltd, 206, 207, 208
britzschka, 87

241

electric, 136, 138
steam, 139, 154, 186, 190
petrol-electric, 139
LGOC X-Type, 140
LGOC B-Type, 140–1, 219
ornithopters, 82
Otto and Langen, 201
overseer, *see* surveyor of highways

pack-horse, 5, 12, 26, 49
pack-team, 46
Palmer, John, 113, 114, 115, 116, 117, 118, 120, 124
Panhard et Levassor, motor car, 202, 203, 208, 209, 213
Papin, Denis, 157
Parnell, Sir Henry, 28, 29, 58
Pascal, Blaise, 127
Patent Steam Wheel and Axle Company, 82
pavement, 48, 49
paving, 56, 57
Pepys, Samuel, 117
and *Diary*, 91
Peugeot motor car, 86, 203
phaeton, 92, 98, 226
'highflyer', 95–6
mail, 112
steam, 187
Pickfords, 221
'pike-keeper's' cottage, *see* toll-house
Pitt, 51, 115, 116
police, 129, 130, 132, 136, 139, 140, 141, 149, 152, 153, 204, 211, 212, 216, 222
Pont Cysyllte, 50
'portable' engine, 191–2, 197
Portland, Duke of, 212
post-chaise, 50, 142, 143, 160, 225, 226
post-coach, 126
posting system, 142–3
Postmaster-General, 28, 30, 113
Public Health Act of 1848, 34
Public Health Act of 1872, 39
Pulteney, Lord, 51

quadricycle, 213

Radcliffe-Ward battery-electric vehicle, 136
railways, 30, 36, 37, 41, 59, 65, 82, 99, 123, 131, 136, 141, 164, 165, 172, 174, 187, 191, 192, 193, 194, 195, 200, 207, 216
Ransomes, Sims and Jefferies, 195
Rational motor cab, 152
'Rebecca Riots', 33
'Red Flag' Act of 1865, 41
Redmund, D., 186
Reform Bill of 1832, 174
Renault motor car, 152–3, 213
Rennie, 58
Richard, Georges, 153
Road Board, 44, 64, 223
road construction,
and ancient trackways, 6–7
and causeways, 10, 45–6
and problem of absorbing water, 46–7
and cambered surfaces, 47, 70
and roof-shaped roads, 47
and the 'road laid wavy', 47
and concave roads, 47–8
and paving of roads, 48–9, 72
and cobbled roads, 48, 72
and methods of surfacing, 50, 59, 61–3
and Telford's work, 50–3
and graded stones, 52–3
and McAdam's work, 50–3
and drainage, 53, 55
and heavy rollers, 55
and dual-surfaced roads, 57
and concrete, 57, 65
and paved roadways, 58
and 'macadamed' roads, 59
and dust problems, 59–60
and road dressing, 61
and tarmac, 62–3, 64, 65
Road Improvement Society, 60
road locomotives, *see* steam road locomotives
road plough, 45